Primary Teacher's Book of Instant WORD GAMES

Over 190 Ready-to-Use Games and Activities
for Any Basal or Whole Language Program!

Primary Teacher's Book of Instant Word Games

Over 190 Ready-to-Use Games and Activities for Any Basal or Whole Language Program!

JUDIE L.H. STROUF

THE CENTER FOR APPLIED RESEARCH IN EDUCATION
West Nyack, New York 10994

Library of Congress Cataloging in Publication Data

Strouf, Judie L. H.,
    Primary teacher's book of instant word games / Judie L. H. Strouf
      p. cm.
    Companion vol. to: Intermediate teacher's book of instant word games.
    ISBN 0-87628-635-X
    1. Educational games. 2. Word games. 3. Puzzles. 4. Language
arts (Primary) 5. Education, Primary–Activity programs.
    I. Strouf, Judie L. H., 1932- Intermediate teacher's book of
instant word games. II. Title

© 1996 *by* The Center for Applied Research in Education, West Nyack, NY

Printed in the United States of America

10 9 8 7 6 5 4 3 2 1

ISBN 0-87628-635-X

Clip Art courtesy of Dover Clip Art Series and Dover Pictorial Archive Series Dover Publications, Inc. Mineola, New York. All other illustrations by Eileen Gerne Ciavarella.

ATTENTION: CORPORATIONS AND SCHOOLS

The Center for Applied Research in Education books are available at quantity discounts with bulk purchase for educational, business, or sales promotional use. For information, please write to: Prentice Hall Career & Personal Development Special Sales, 113 Sylvan Avenue, Englewood Cliffs, NJ 07632. Please supply: title of book, ISBN number, quantity, how the book will be used, date needed.

**THE CENTER FOR APPLIED RESEARCH
IN EDUCATION**
West Nyack, NY 10994
A Simon & Schuster Company

On the World Wide Web at http://www.phdirect.com

Prentice Hall International (UK) Limited, *London*
Prentice Hall of Australia Pty. Limited, *Sydney*
Prentice Hall Canada, Inc., *Toronto*
Prentice Hall Hispanoamericana, S.A., *Mexico*
Prentice Hall of India Private Limited, *New Delhi*
Prentice Hall of Japan, Inc., *Tokyo*
Simon & Schuster Asia Pte. Ltd., *Singapore*
Editora Prentice Hall do Brasil, Ltda., *Rio de Janeiro*

ABOUT THE AUTHOR

Judie Strouf is an experienced educator and author of materials for elementary and secondary teachers. Her teaching certificates and degrees are from Central Michigan University and Western Michigan University. In addition, she has taken advanced training at the University of Michigan and was the recipient of a Fulbright Scholarship from the United States Office of Education in Washington, D.C., to serve as an exchange teacher in England. She has traveled extensively, studying educational institutions and supervising student teachers both here and abroad.

Her major teaching and counseling experiences have been at Harper Creek Community Schools in Battle Creek, Michigan; Harbor Springs Community Schools in Harbor Springs, Michigan; and Chipping Norton Grammar School in Chipping Norton, England.

OTHER BOOKS BY THIS AUTHOR

Hooked on Language Arts! Ready-to-Use Activities and Worksheets for Grades 4–8, The Center for Applied Research in Education, West Nyack, New York, 1990.

Americas Discovery Activities Kit: Ready-to-Use Worksheets for the Age of Exploration, The Center for Applied Research in Education, West Nyack, New York, 1991.

Hooked on the U.S.A.: Activities for Studying the States, J. Weston Walch, Portland, Maine, 1993.

The Literature Teacher's Book of Lists, The Center for Applied Research in Education, West Nyack, New York, 1993.

Intermediate Teacher's Book of Instant Word Games, The Center for Applied Research in Education, West Nyack, New York, 1996.

ABOUT THIS RESOURCE

Why bother with games and puzzles?

Word games and puzzles deliver an added dimension to any curricula, but stimulating, fun activities are *essential* for primary teachers. Short attention spans and the constant need for reinforcement throughout these early grades dictate that effective teachers incorporate supplementary, "lighter" materials.

Specific benefits of games and puzzles:

- Release tension and energy
- Challenge faster thinkers
- Enhance self concept
- Improve problem-solving skills
- Promote cooperative group behavior
- Develop positive feeling for language
- Turn extra or wasted time into productive learning
- Help relax and heal by evoking laughter
- Capture attention of reluctant learners
- Provide focus on particular skills or concepts
- Allow teacher *or* student leadership
- Furnish change of pace
- Avert boredom
- Require minimal, if any, teacher preparation

A positive feature of *Primary Teacher's Book of Instant Word Games* is that, in addition to the usual word search, crossword, maze, and dot-connecting puzzles commonly found in most puzzle and game books, a wide range of OTHER techniques and devices are also employed, such as:

Original alphabet book

Pictograms

Codes

Scrambled words and anagrams

Roundabouts

Word squares and ladders

Picture puzzles

Human spelling

Word chains

Hidden messages

Tic-tac-toe

Board games

Team relays

Guessing games

Word-pattern activities

Word wheels

Flash and response cards

Spelling and alphabet puzzles

Riddles

This collection of 197 *student-tested* activities (individual puzzles, as well as group games) is based on the *essential elements and competencies commonly taught in grades 1–3.* It is a logical companion to *Intermediate Teacher's Book of Instant Word Games* designed for grades 4–6. Reading, library skills, spelling, and vocabulary are predominate. However, about one-fourth of the activities involve literacy enrichment and skills in the content areas of mathematics, social studies, and science.

The projects are practical, whether you use a basal text or whole language approach. You can use these ideas to introduce a concept, add to regular lessons, follow-up after teaching, reward early finishers, or as sponge activities. Enjoyable, content-oriented challenges add spice to your classes and help children avoid boredom that can result from the inevitable drill needed to develop and maintain skills at these early ages.

The games focus on making all students "winners." Children win because they get practice in various skills and develop competencies needed for effective communication. Individual competition is down-played, while group, partnership, and team spirit is encouraged. As many students as possible are fully engaged during an activity, rather than being "losers," called "out," sitting down, or otherwise temporarily banished from the game. This important educational principle distinguishes this word game book from many other self-described "game books."

Activities are not labeled by grade levels because of the massive variance in abilities among students in single classrooms and among school curricula in different geographical areas. The puzzles range from very simple with obvious answers to those complex enough for the gifted child. After minimal experimentation, you will find the instant word games and puzzles that excite *your* pupils and most efficiently accomplish your goals. You will be amazed and gratified when students ask you to let them play certain games. Usually the simplest, easiest to play, and fastest-moving become their favorites.

Don't miss the APPENDICES, which include complete answer keys and special hints on using games and puzzles with your students, instructions for making or using specific items, and occasional comments on grade appropriateness or vocabulary level. These teacher notes are referred to throughout the text with the notation N-1 through N-22 in the upper right-hand corner of some of the pages.

To have real value, word games should be more than diversions, busy-work, or time-fillers. This collection is designed to be educationally sound and relevant to the present primary curriculum. The instant word games and puzzles will create enthusiasm and capture the cooperative and competitive spirits of your children. Your students will learn AND enjoy, and isn't that the most rewarding combination possible?

Judie L. H. Strouf

TABLE OF CONTENTS

SECTION ONE

Reading and Library
1

Individual Reproducibles

Group Games and Materials

SECTION TWO

Spelling and Vocabulary
95

Individual Reproducibles

Group Games and Materials

SECTION THREE

Language Arts, Mathematics, Social Studies, and Science
171

Individual Reproducibles (Language Arts)

Group Games and Materials

Individual Reproducibles (Mathematics)

APPENDIX ONE

Generic Aids
221

APPENDIX TWO

For the Teacher Only
231

APPENDIX THREE

Teacher Notes N-1 through N-22
235

APPENDIX FOUR

Answer Key
241

Section One

READING AND LIBRARY

1–1 LETTER DISCRIMINATION

Letters are just like code symbols. Each symbol or letter has its own meaning. Below are code symbols and letters mixed together. Circle all the letters of the alphabet. Make sure each letter is in the same order as it is in the alphabet. Go past any that are out of order.

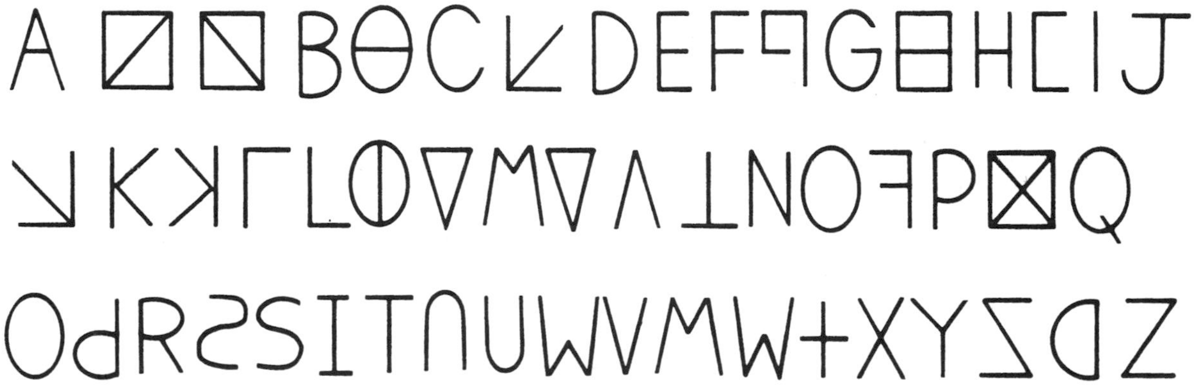

A ⊠ ⊡ ◸ B Θ C ∠ D E F ¶ G ⊖ H ⊏ i J

↓ K ⋉ Γ L ◍ ∇ M ∀ ⊥ N O Ⅎ P ⊠ Q

O d R � I T ∩ U W ∨ M + X Y ∫ ⊓ Z

1–2 ALPHABET CONNECTION

Begin at the top with *A*. Then move down, up, right, left, or diagonally to connect all the letters in the alphabet in order. Make an alphabet connection!

Begin
↓

A	B	C	A	D	E	F
L	K	B	J	I	H	G
M	N	C	O	E	P	Q
V	U	T	D	S	F	R
W	X	Y	Z	G	A	C
E	G	I	I	H	K	M
O	Q	J	S	U	W	L
Y	B	D	K	F	H	J
L	N	P	L	R	T	V
X	N	M	Z	B	C	D
J	O	I	H	G	F	E
K	L	P	M	R	N	O
A	S	W	Q	C	S	B
V	C	X	M	T	O	Y
Q	W	E	U	R	T	P
A	S	V	D	F	G	H
Z	R	W	C	V	B	N
P	X	O	I	U	Y	T
Y	A	D	G	J	L	M
M	Z	N	B	V	C	Z

↑
End

1–3 QWERTY ALPHABITS

Knowing the alphabet helps us learn how to read, locate information, and use glossaries, telephone books, dictionaries, computers, and typewriters. The diagram below shows the letters of the alphabet as they usually appear on computer or typewriter keys.

(Q) (W) (E) (R) (T) (Y) (U) (I) (O) (P)

(A) (S) (D) (F) (G) (H) (J) (K) (L)

(Z) (X) (C) (V) (B) (N) (M)

On the keys below, write the letters in *alphabetical* order. The first key is done for you.

(A) ( ) ( ) ( ) ( ) ( ) ( ) ( ) ( ) ( )

( ) ( ) ( ) ( ) ( ) ( ) ( ) ( ) ( )

( ) ( ) ( ) ( ) ( ) ( ) ( )

1–4 ALPHABET SCRAMBLE

Use one letter of the alphabet in each blank square to form a word of three to five letters. All words except one are taken from spelling lists for grades 1–3. *Use each letter only once!*

1.	B	S	T		R	O	W
2.	A	P	O		U	I	T
3.	G	A	M		C	F	T
4.	D	Z	F		I	N	G
5.	X	U	B		O	C	K
6.	W	G	N		C	T	V
7.	Y	L	O		E	L	P
8.	N	M	A		B	C	D
9.	K	D	O		E	F	Q
10.	H	C	L		B	G	K
11.	U	I	J		U	M	P
12.	I	B	O		S	H	J
13.	J	I	A		I	K	E

14.	A	M	A		E	F	W
15.	N	S	I		E	B	E
16.	D	V	C		O	S	E
17.	R	O	O		D	C	X
18.	M	B	U		Y	Z	W
19.	E	L	U		K	F	M
20.	L	B	O		E	S	Z
21.	L	K	O		F	G	B
22.	H	P	E		R	V	N
23.	T	S	H		S	Q	R
24.	B	U	Z		A	Q	R
25.	S	M	I		E	P	U
26.	T	Q	B		N	E	O

CIRCLE THE LETTER OF THE ALPHABET AFTER YOU USE IT.

A   B   C   D   E   F   G   H   I   J   K   L   M

N   O   P   Q   R   S   T   U   V   W   X   Y   Z

© 1996 by The Center for Applied Research in Education

1–5 GIVE ME AN <u>A</u>

I   a m   a n   a l k i n.

Everything I like begins with the letter <u>a</u> and has a SHORT <u>a</u> sound. Circle the word that I would choose from each box and write it on the line shown.

I eat: animals | ants
               apples | adding
                                                | about
        _____

I live in: Africa | across
               attics | anthills
                                                | all
        _____

1–6 GIVE ME A B

I am a b o s i t.

Everything I like begins with the letter b. Circle the word that I would choose from each box and write it on the line shown.

I eat: balls | rugs |
                                                       | bugs |
              bats | pegs |

              _____

I live in: barns | dens |
                                                       | guns |
              boats | bushes |

              _____

1–7 GIVE ME A <u>C</u>

I a m a c a v i d.

Everything I like begins with the letter <u>c</u>. Circle the word that I would choose from each box and write it on the line shown.

I eat: corn

                 carrots

_____

cold
cake
cry

I live in: castles

                 clouds

_____

caves
chew
kite

1–8 GIVE ME A <u>D</u>

I am a d o r a l.

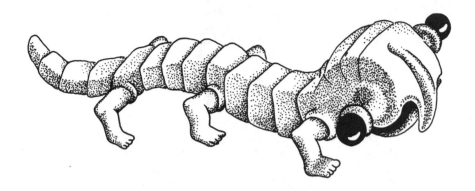

Everything I like begins with the letter <u>d</u>. Circle the word that I would choose from each box and write it on the line shown.

I eat: dishes

ducks

_____

| boots |
| dirt |
| bears |

I live in: drums

dust

_____

| deep |
| boxes |
| desks |

1–9 GIVE ME AN E

I a m a n e s t a n.

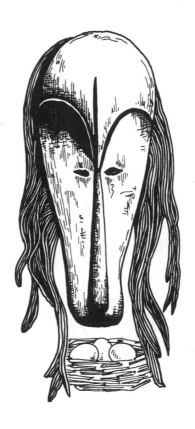

Everything I like begins with the letter e and has a SHORT e sound. Circle the word that I would choose from each box and write it on the line shown.

I eat: elks

                 elephants

                 _____

end

enough

eggs

I live in: envelopes

                 elevators

                 _____

eyes

eat

elms

1–10 GIVE ME AN F

I am a fibot.

Everything I like begins with the letter f. Circle the word that I would choose from each box and write it on the line shown.

I eat: frogs

              fish

              _____

| figs |
| pigs |
| fun |

I live in: fishponds

              flowers

              _____

| friend |
| forests |
| party |

1–11 GIVE ME A <u>G</u>

I am a g u r a b.

Everything I like begins with the letter g. Circle the word that I would choose from each box and write it on the line shown.

I eat: goldfish

        geese

_____

grapes

pens

get

I live in: ground

        grass

_____

grow

girl

gates

1–12 GIVE ME AN H

I am a h e m u s.

© 1996 by The Center for Applied Research in Education

Everything I like begins with the letter h. Circle the word that I would choose from each box and write it on the line shown.

I eat: horses

                hares

                _____

hay
nets
has

I live in: houses

                hills

                _____

happen
hook
holes

1–13 GIVE ME AN I̱

I a m a n i s b u n.

Everything I like begins with the letter i̱ and has a SHORT i̱ sound. Circle the word that I would choose from each box and write it on the line shown.

I eat: impalas

                inchworms

                _____

idea
insects
is

I live in: inns

                instruments

                _____

into
India
ice

1–14 GIVE ME A J

I am a j a r o w.

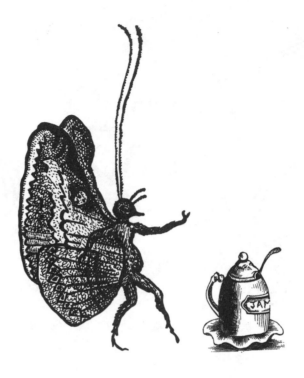

Everything I like begins with the letter j. Circle the word that I would choose from each box and write it on the line shown.

I eat: jam | five |
              junk | juice |
                                                               | just |

              _____

I live in: jugs | jump |
              jars | jeans |
                                                               | jokes |

              _____

1–15 GIVE ME A **K**

I a m a k o z e c.

© 1996 by The Center for Applied Research in Education

Everything I like begins with the letter **k**. Circle the word that I would choose from each box and write it on the line shown.

I eat: ketchup

             kekabs

             _____

| key |
| kiss |
| kale |

I live in: kennels

             kites

             _____

| keep |
| king |
| kitchens |

1–16 GIVE ME AN L

I a m a l i x u r.

Everything I like begins with the letter l. Circle the word that I would choose from each box and write it on the line shown.

I eat: lambs

            lunch

            _____

lions
little
looks

I live in: lawns

            logs

            _____

lists
lakes
learn

1–17 GIVE ME AN <u>M</u>

I a m a m u l e t.

Everything I like begins with the letter <u>m</u>. Circle the word that I would choose from each box and write it on the line shown.

I eat: mice

               milk

_____

neat
dinner
moths

I live in: mops

               mud

_____

movie
mouse
mountains

1–18 GIVE ME AN N

I am a nesam.

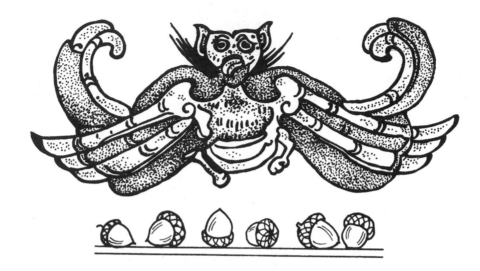

Everything I like begins with the letter <u>n</u>. Circle the word that I would choose from each box and write it on the line shown.

I eat: nuts

               noodles

               _____

| meat |
| names |
| notebooks |

I live in: newspapers

               neighborhoods

               _____

| nests |
| move |
| next |

1–19 GIVE ME AN O̲

I   a m   a n   o x f e r.

Everything I like begins with the letter o̲ and has a SHORT o̲ sound. Circle the word that I would choose from each box and write it on the line shown.

I eat: ocelots

                otters

                _____

once
olives
ovens

I live in: oxen

                opera houses

                _____

octopuses
oceans
over

1–20 GIVE ME A P

I am a p a k a w.

© 1996 by The Center for Applied Research in Education

Everything I like begins with the letter p. Circle the word that I would choose from each box and write it on the line shown.

I eat: popcorn

peanuts

_____

| places |
| pancakes |
| question |

I live in: parks

ponds

_____

| dinosaur |
| puddles |
| pencil |

1–21 GIVE ME A Q

I am a q u l i r.

Everything I like begins with the letter q. Circle the word that I would choose from each box and write it on the line shown.

I eat: quiche

                   quills

                   _____

| grill |
| quail |
| guilt |

I live in: quarters

                   quicksand

                   _____

| goose |
| quit |
| quilts |

1–22 GIVE ME AN R

I am a ronip.

Everything I like begins with the letter r. Circle the word that I would choose from each box and write it on the line shown.

I eat: robins

                rabbits

                _____

| roses |
| noses |
| robber |

I live in: rainbows

                rivers

                _____

| rocks |
| socks |
| ride |

1–23 GIVE ME AN <u>S</u>

I am a s i j a k.

Everything I like begins with the letter <u>s</u>. Circle the word that I would choose from each box and write it on the line shown.

I eat: sheep

              snakes

              _____

street
seeds
weeds

I live in: sand

              stumps

              _____

coil
soil
spoil

1–24 GIVE ME A T

I am a t e h o r.

Everything I like begins with the letter t. Circle the word that I would choose from each box and write it on the line shown.

I eat: turtles

                turkeys

                _____

think
toads
lights

I live in: treetops

                tents

                _____

taken
threw
tugboats

1–25 GIVE ME A <u>U</u>

I   a m   a n   u n d a x.

Everything I like begins with the letter <u>u</u> and has a SHORT <u>u</u> sound. Circle the word that I would choose from each box and write it on the line shown.

I eat: ushers

                umpires

                _____

| uncles |
| vampires |
| use |

I live in: uplands

                undershirts

                _____

| until |
| vines |
| umbrellas |

1–26 GIVE ME A <u>V</u>

I am a vaxof.

Everything I like begins with the letter <u>v</u>. Circle the word that I would choose from each box and write it on the line shown.

I eat: vegetables

            violets

_____

over
very
varmints

I live in: valleys

            villages

_____

vans
vane
waits

1–27 GIVE ME A <u>W</u>

I   a m   a   w u m e t.

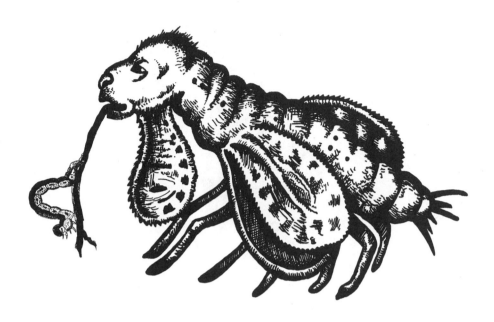

Everything I like begins with the letter <u>w</u>. Circle the word that I would choose from each box and write it on the line shown.

I eat: wood

                whiskers

                _____

| worms |
| weather |
| walked |

I live in: windowsills

                webs

                _____

| doors |
| wells |
| moors |

1–28 GIVE ME AN X

I   a m   a   x i g a r.

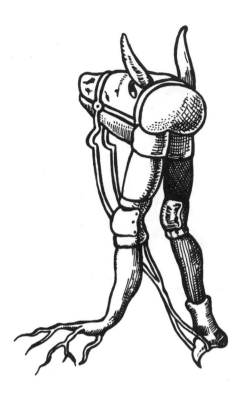

© 1996 by The Center for Applied Research in Education

Everything I like begins with the letter <u>x</u>. Circle the word that I would choose from each box and write it on the line shown.

I eat: xerophyte

xylene

_____

foxes
zigzag
xenon

I live in: xylophones

x-rays

_____

Xanthus
excuses
buzz

1–29 GIVE ME A Y

I a m a y o r a b.

Everything I like begins with the letter y. Circle the word that I would choose from each box and write it on the line shown.

I eat: yolks

  yams

  _____

| |
| year |
| yelled |
| yarn |

I live in: yachts

  yawls

  _____

| |
| yards |
| guards |
| yellow |

1–30 GIVE ME A <u>Z</u>

I a m a z e n o x.

Everything I like begins with the letter <u>z</u>. Circle the word that I would choose from each box and write it on the line shown.

I eat: zucchini

              zebras

              _____

zippers
gizzards
zap

I live in: Zaire

              Zanzibar

              _____

zoos
ZIP Code
zone

1–31 PAIRS O' SHOES

Pair the words from the SHOE STORE that have the same *two beginning letters*. Write the first two matching letters in the heel of the shoe. Write the matching words in the front of the shoe. See the example.

SHOE STORE

slam

cross

chop

whale

club

chin

small

slow

drip

criss

clown

smile

drop

street

white

stop

1. ch | chin
   ch | chop

2. cl

3. cr

4. sl

5. sm

6. st

7. dr

8. wh

1–32 BOXED PAIRS

Pair the words from the WORD BANK that have the same *two beginning letters*. Print the first two matching letters at the beginning of the box. Print the whole word in the other parts of the box. The first one is done for you.

1.

th	thank
	them

6.

2.

3.

7.

4.

8.

5.

9.

© 1996 by The Center for Applied Research in Education

WORD BANK

black	glad	snip
green	frog	ship
brown	glass	them
short	grass	frown
snap	flag	flew
blend	brick	thank

1–33 <u>SH</u> SOUNDS

Pick the flowers that have the same <u>sh</u> sound as <u>ship</u>. Put them in the vase by filling in the words in the flowers in the vase.

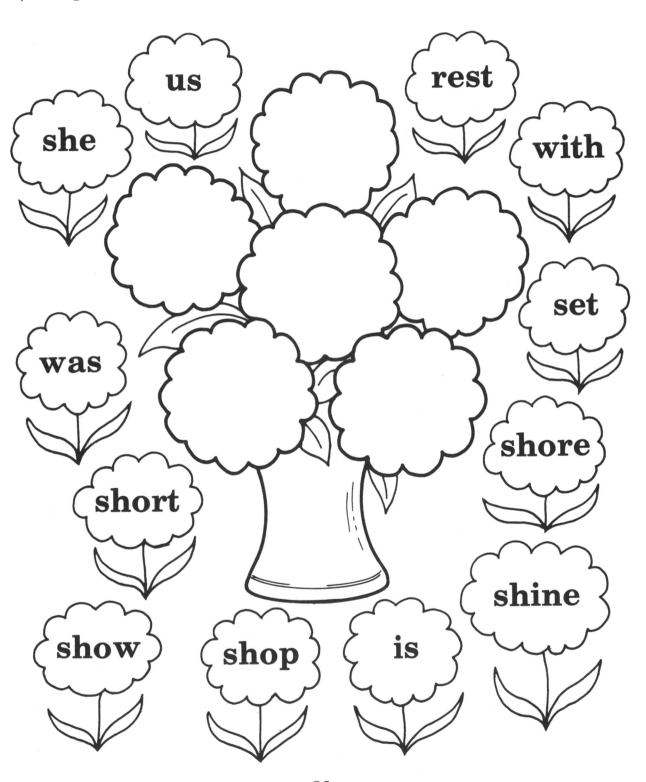

1–34 **TH** SOUNDS

Go up the road with th sounds. Choose the words that have the same sound as the th in bath. Put them IN ORDER next to the mile markers on the road. Drive carefully!

WORD BANK

lunch

mouth

path

train

with

three

teeth

thanks

than

which

they

thirst

both

north

cash

thick

store

those

moth

Thursday

dust

End

Mile 12 _____

Mile 11 _____

Mile 10 _____

Mile 9 _____

Mile 8 _____

Mile 7 _____

Mile 6 _____

Mile 5 _____

Mile 4 _____

Mile 3 _____

Mile 2 _____

Mile 1 _____

Start

1–35 SILENT CONSONANTS

The first column shows the dictionary pronunciation of the words. Sound out the word. The second column shows any silent consonants. Try to spell the word correctly in the last column, being sure to use the silent letters.
HINT: Sometimes <u>k</u> sounds like <u>k</u>, but sometimes <u>k</u> sounds like <u>c</u>.

PRONUNCIATION	SILENT LETTERS	SPELLING
1. līt	gh	
2. klĭm	b	
3. wôk	l	
4. lăm	b	
5. nīt	gh	
6. kăs'l	t/e	
7. sī	gh	
8. thŭm	b	

1–36 SHORT VOWEL SOUNDS

Pick the apples off the tree that have words with short vowel sounds. Put them on the blanks in the applesauce below.

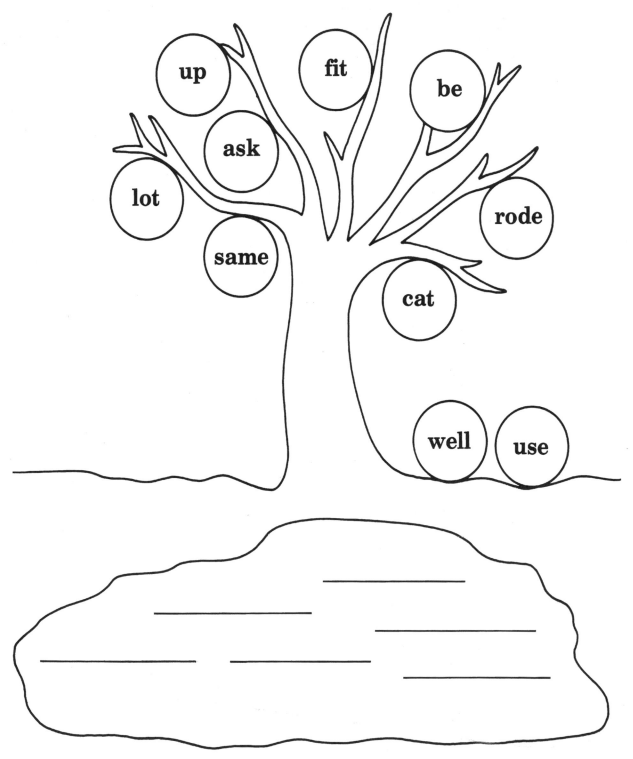

1–37 SILENT LETTERS

All these words have silent letters. Add the fronts and backs to spell them correctly. Cross out the fronts and backs as you use them. You will use them all. After you fill out the words, circle the silent letters.

1. _____   N   O   _____

2. _____   I   G   _____

3. _____   H   O   U   L   _____

4. _____   H   _____

5. _____   A   M   _____

6. _____   I   G   H   _____

FRONTS
W   N   S   H   G   K

BACKS
D   H   O   W   E   T

1–38 SILLY PARAGRAPH (FINAL E)

Here is a silly paragraph. It sounds silly because final e's have been added where not needed, and final e's have been left out where they should have been. Write your new words on the lines below so that the story makes more sense.

HINT: The final silent e makes the other vowel have a long sound (man becomes mane).

On a (1) fin day in May a (2) mane (3) rod into town in his (4) vane. His (5) hate was black; his suit was (6) whit. He walked with a (7) can, and (8) note very (9) fare.

"(10) Cane you read this (11) cod while you (12) shin my shoe?" he said. Then he handed me a (13) not.

"I (14) hop so," I replied, "but in this (15) dime light I can't tell a (16) dote from a dash!"

1. _____   9. _____

2. _____   10. _____

3. _____   11. _____

4. _____   12. _____

5. _____   13. _____

6. _____   14. _____

7. _____   15. _____

8. _____   16. _____

Name _____

1–39 MUSICAL NOTES

Find the syllable representing each tone on the musical diatonic scale. Use the NOTE KEYS to help you. Write the syllable on the blank under each note.

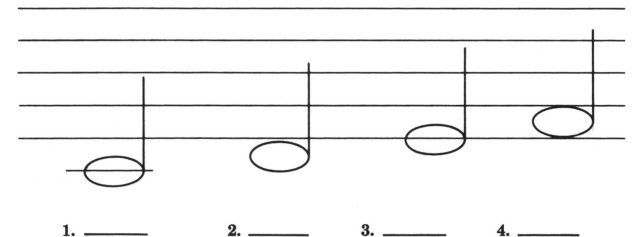

1. _____   2. _____   3. _____   4. _____

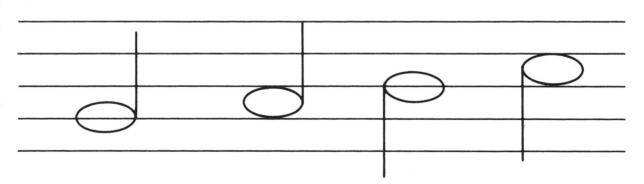

5. _____   6. _____   7. _____   8. _____

NOTE KEYS			
do	fa	mi	sol
do	la	re	ti

1–40 SILLY SYLLABLES

Use the syllables in the SILLY SYLLABLES box to form words that fit the clues given. All the words relate to reading or research. Write your words on the lines shown.

CLUES

1. highly imaginative writing

___ ___ ___   ___ ___   S ___

2. reference book

___ ___   ___ Y ___ ___ ___ ___ ___ ___ ___ ___ ___

3. name of written work

___ ___   ___ L ___

4. writer of plays

___ L ___ ___   ___ ___ ___ ___ ___ ___ ___

5. writer

A ___   ___ ___ ___ ___

6. life story by another

B___   ___ ___   ___ ___   ___ ___ ___

7. story with a lesson

___ ___   ___ L ___

8. alphabetical contents

___ ___   ___ E ___

© 1996 by The Center for Applied Research in Education

SILLY SYLLABLES					
A	AU	BLE	CLO	CY	DEX
EN	FA	FAN	I	IN	OG
OR	PED	PHY	PLAY	RA	SY
TA	TI	THOR	TLE	WRIGHT	

Name _____

1–41 TEST YOUR LOGIC

Five boys came to America from other countries and each had a different color hair. Given the clues below, fill in the chart so each boy is matched with his country and hair color.

	MARIO	JUAN	NIGEL	HANS	CHARLES
COUNTRY					
HAIR COLOR					

1. Mario is from Italy.

2. Hans has yellow hair.

3. The black-haired boy is from Mexico.

4. Nigel does not have brown hair.

5. The Englishman has red hair.

6. Hans is not from Canada.

7. Charles has grey hair.

8. Juan is not from Germany

9. Nigel is from England.

Name _____

1–42 SEQUENCE

The following sentences are mixed up. If they are straightened out, they will form two separate paragraphs. See if you can put them in proper sequence by <u>number</u>.

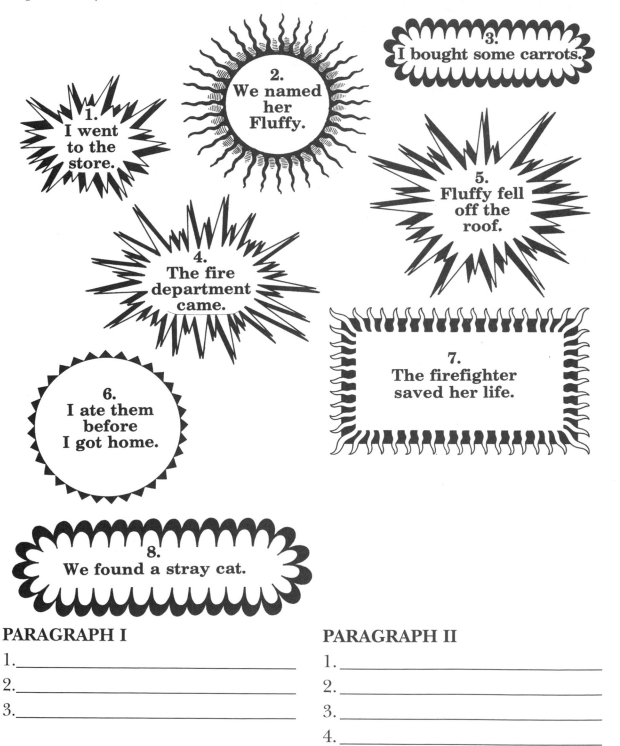

1. I went to the store.

2. We named her Fluffy.

3. I bought some carrots.

4. The fire department came.

5. Fluffy fell off the roof.

6. I ate them before I got home.

7. The firefighter saved her life.

8. We found a stray cat.

PARAGRAPH I

1._____

2._____

3._____

PARAGRAPH II

1._____

2._____

3._____

4._____

5._____

1–43 CALL TO ORDER

Put these pictures in order so they tell a story. Show the order by numbering the picture that should come first as picture <u>1</u>; the second picture in the story, <u>2</u>, and so on.

1–44 ROWS AND COLUMNS

Rows run across the page (a through e); columns run up and down (1 through 6). Follow the directions below. Then unscramble the leftover letters to find out what is in the library.

LIBRARY

	1	2	3	4	5	6
a	P	O	S	Q	O	P
b	B	A	E	I	O	U
c	O	X	V	T	P	G
d	S	D	P	O	Q	T
e	W	B	Z	Q	K	P

1. Cross out **P**'s and **Q**'s.

2. Cross out consonants in **column 1**.

3. Cross out letters in **row c** that come after **S**.

4. Cross out **Z**'s and **T**'s.

5. Cross out vowels in **row b**.

6. Unscramble the rest of the letters to form two words.

WHAT IS FOUND IN THE LIBRARY?

___ ___ ___ ___   ___ ___ ___ ___ ___

1–45 CATEGORIES

Can you think of words beginning with the letters below that fit into the categories in the columns? There is more than one correct answer. You will get a chance to share them after everyone is done.

MONTHS

M _____

A _____

O _____

F _____

S _____

STATES

M _____

A _____

O _____

F _____

S _____

FOODS

M _____

A _____

O _____

F _____

S _____

1–46 SCATTERGORIZE

A category is a group of items that have something in common. The items below are in alphabetical order instead of by category. Choose <u>one</u> category and write all the words that belong in the group on the lines provided. If you have extra time, try to unscatter the rest. **HINT**: There are ten items in each category.

bat
bird
black
blue
brown
cat
dog
duck
eight
five

four
fox
frog
grey
green
hen
horse
nine
one
orange

pig
pink
red
seven
six
ten
three
two
white
yellow

ANIMALS

_____

_____

_____

_____

_____

_____

_____

_____

_____

_____

COLORS

_____

_____

_____

_____

_____

_____

_____

_____

_____

_____

NUMBERS

_____

_____

_____

_____

_____

_____

_____

_____

_____

_____

Name _____

1–47 ODD MAN OUT

Circle the word in each group that does not fit. Then write the sentence the remaining words make.

1.
I	run
jump	play

2.
blue	red
grey	can

3.
one	two
do	four

4.
you	good
me	we

5.
yes	no
maybe	work

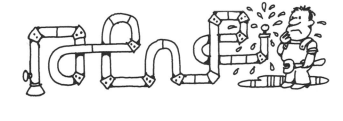

SENTENCE: _____

_____

_____

_____

_____

1–48 SHAPES AND CATEGORIES

Let's see if you can group things that are alike into the same category. Observe the drawing, follow the directions, and answer the questions.

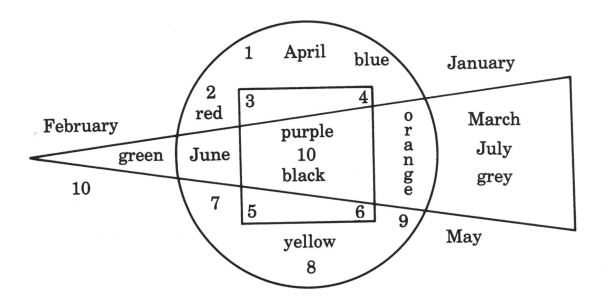

© 1996 by The Center for Applied Research in Education

1. How many colors are in the circle? _____

   List them. _____

   _____

2. How many numbers are in the square? _____

   List them. _____

   _____

3. How many months are in the triangle?

   List them. _____

   _____

1–49 INSTRUMENT FAMILIES

To make music on stringed instruments you pluck, bow, or hammer. Wind instruments are blown into directly or have a reed. Percussion instruments are struck to make sounds. Sort the common instruments from the MUSIC STORE into their proper categories.

STRINGS

1. _____
2. _____
3. _____
4. _____
5. _____
6. _____

WINDS

7. _____
8. _____
9. _____
10. _____
11. _____
12. _____
13. _____
14. _____
15. _____
16. _____
17. _____

PERCUSSION

18. _____
19. _____
20. _____
21. _____
22. _____
23. _____

MUSIC STORE

harp	English horn
xylophone	French horn
violin	viola
piccolo	triangle
oboe	chimes
bassoon	flute
trombone	bass
drums	trumpet
cymbals	tuba
piano	saxophone
cello	clarinet
glockenspiel	

1–50 CATEGORIES: BIGGER AND BIGGER

Putting subjects into categories helps us find information in the library. Sometimes you must go to larger and larger categories before you find a listing and locate what you are looking for.

Here is a scrambled listing of subject categories. Unscramble them into separate categories with each list going from smallest to largest. Parts of each category are done for you. See if you can finish the puzzle.

EXAMPLE: 1. Angora; 2. cat; 3. domestic animals.

SCRAMBLED SUBJECTS

fish	transportation	baseball
clarinet	puck	orchestra
summer sports	agriculture	telephone
Red Sox	Chevrolet	collections
democracy	communication	ice hockey
stamps	goldfish	winter sports
music	fruit	apple
automobile	government	aquarium
Senate	hobbies	cellular phone

---

1. apple

2. _____

3. _____

4. _____

5. Chevrolet

6. _____

7. _____

8. _____

9. communication

10. _____

11. fish

12. _____

13. _____

14. _____

15. summer sports

16. Senate

17. _____

18. _____

19. puck

20. _____

21. _____

22. _____

23. hobbies

24. _____

25. _____

26. orchestra

27. _____

1–51 PICK UP THE TAIL

Write words in each category, being careful to "pick up the tail" letter of the preceding word in the list.
   EXAMPLE: (Verbs) ra<u>n</u>; <u>na</u>b; <u>b</u>ark.

VERBS

_____   _____   _____

_____   _____   _____

_____   _____   _____

_____   _____   _____

NOUNS

_____   _____   _____

_____   _____   _____

_____   _____   _____

_____   _____   _____

FOODS

_____   _____

_____   _____

_____   _____

_____   _____

PLACES (CITIES OR COUNTRIES)

_____   _____

_____   _____

_____   _____

_____   _____

1–52 WHAT PART OF A BOOK AM I?

See if you can answer the riddles. Each answer deals with books.

1. I am on the outside.

   I can be hard or soft.

   I keep the pages clean and straight.

   What am I? _____

2. I am on the edge.

   I have letters and numbers.

   I help the book stand up.

   What am I? _____

3. I am on the front.

   I have a special page inside.

   I tell the book's name.

   What am I? _____

4. I think the thoughts.

   I put them together.

   I write the book.

   Who am I? _____

5. I have imagination.

   I make a book look interesting.

   I draw the pictures.

   Who am I? _____

1–53 NURSERY RHYME PUZZLE

See if you can guess these nursery rhymes from the clues. They are proba-bly all rhymes you read when you were younger.

```
        E
    D farmer L
        L
```

```
SIM PLE
    ON
```

```
GE ORGIE
 P
```

1. _____

_____

2. _____

_____

3. _____

_____

4. _____

_____

5. _____

_____

6. _____

_____

7. _____

_____

8. _____

_____

1-54 MOTHER GOOSE AND FRIENDS

All the words in the puzzle come from Mother Goose or other well-known nursery rhymes. See how many you can remember.

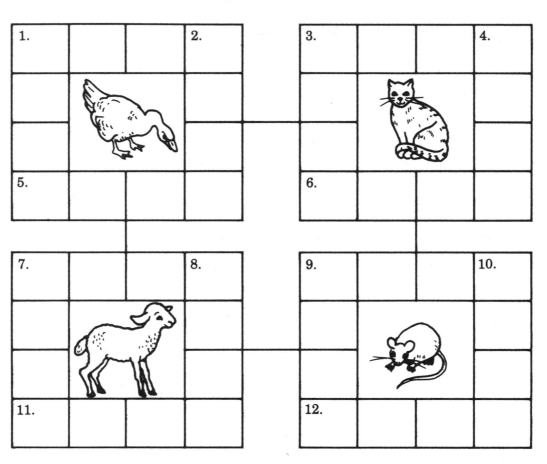

ACROSS

1. Mary had a little ____
3. Humpty Dumpty sat on a ____
5. Once upon a ____
6. The ____ and the unicorn
7. Jack Horner pulled out a ____
9. Hickory, dickory, ____
11. King Cole called for his ____
12. Mother Hubbard's poor dog had ____

DOWN

1. Three kittens ____ their mittens
2. Little Boy ____
3. Black sheep, have you any ____
4. Jack Sprat's wife could eat no ____
7. Little Bo ____
8. Three blind ____
9. Jack fell ____ and broke his crown
10. Bobby Shafto had buckles at his ____

1–55 LITTLE ONES (EASY)

Many stories or characters have "LITTLE" in their titles. See how many little ones you can remember. Use the clues to help you. Use capital letters on names or important words in titles.

1. LITTLE ___ ___   ___ ___ ___ ___ (tended sheep)

2. LITTLE ___ ___ ___ ___   ___ ___ ___ ___ ___ ___
   (sat in a corner)

3. LITTLE ___ ___ ___ ___ ___ (by Louisa May Alcott)

4. LITTLE ___ ___ ___ (by Louisa May Alcott)

5. LITTLE ___ ___ ___ ___ ___   ___ ___

   ___ ___ ___ ___   ___ ___ ___ ___ ___ ___ ___
   (TV series)

6. LITTLE ___ ___ ___   ___ ___ ___ ___ ___ ___

   ___ ___ ___ ___ (met a bad wolf)

7. LITTLE ___ ___ ___ ___   ___ ___ ___ ___ ___ ___
   (sat on a tuffet)

8. LITTLE ___ ___ ___   ___ ___ ___ ___ (was asked to
   blow his horn)

9. LITTLE ___ ___ ___ ___

   ___ ___ ___ ___ ___ ___ (sang for his supper)

10. LITTLE ___ ___ ___ ___ (Robin Hood character)

1–56 LITTLE ONES (HARDER)

Many stories or characters have "LITTLE" in their titles. See how many little ones you can remember. Use the clues to help you. Use capital letters on any important words in the title.

1. The LITTLE ___ ___ ___ ___ ___ ___ (rhymes with wince)

2. Three LITTLE ___ ___ ___ ___ (fairy tale)

3. ___ ___ ___ ___ ___ ___ ___ LITTLE ("the sky is falling")

4. LITTLE ___ ___ ___ ___ ___   ___ ___

___ ___ ___ ___ ___ ___   ___ ___ ___ ___ ___
(by Laura Ingalls Wilder)

5. LITTLE ___ ___ ___ ___ ___

___ ___ ___ ___ ___ ___ ___ ___ ___ (sat in the cinders)

6. ___ ___ ___ ___ ___ ___ LITTLE (by E. B. White)

7. LITTLE ___ ___ ___ ___ ___

___ ___ ___ ___ ___ ___ ___ ___ ___ (a bird)

8. A LITTLE ___ ___ ___   ___ ___ ___ ___ (rhymes with "toy cost")

9. The LITTLE ___ ___ ___ ___ ___

___ ___ ___ ___ ___ (color plus animal)

10. The LITTLE ___ ___ ___   ___ ___ ___ (folk tale with a lesson)

11. The LITTLE ___ ___ ___ ___ ___ ___ ___ ___ (by Frances Hodgson Burnett)

12. The LITTLE ___ ___ ___ ___ ___

___ ___ ___ ___ ___   ___ ___ ___ ___ ___ ("I *think* I can")

Name _____

1–57 BOOK OR STORY TITLES

Can you identify these books or story titles from the clues?

woman woman woman woman

 WHITE +

dwarf   dwarf   dwarf
dwarf   dwarf   dwarf   dwarf

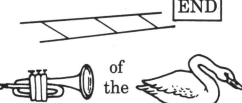 END

million   million
million   million

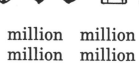

1._____

_____

2._____

_____

3._____

_____

4._____

_____

5._____

_____

6._____

_____

7._____

_____

8._____

_____

9._____

_____

10._____

_____

1–58 STORY FUN

Answer the questions. Cross out the letters of your answers that are in the row with the same number as the question. When you are done, the letters that are left will tell you what you are (at the bottom of the page).

EXAMPLE: If the answer to question 1 was <u>yes</u>, you would cross out <u>y</u> and <u>e</u> and <u>s</u> going across in Row 1. That would leave the letter <u>r</u>. (Of course, this ISN'T the right answer!)

Row 1	E	R	Y	S
Row 2	G	M	O	D
Row 3	G	E	A	G
Row 4	R	Z	O	T
Row 5	M	H	Y	A

1. Who wrote <u>Curious George</u>? _____

2. What kind of animal was Clifford? _____

3. What did Horton hatch? _____

4. Baum wrote <u>The Wizard of</u> what? _____

5. What goes with "Green Eggs"? _____

Y O U   A R E   A   ☐ ☐ ☐ ☐ ☐ ☐

© 1996 by The Center for Applied Research in Education

Name _____

1–59 COUNT YOUR READING

These titles all contain numbers. See if you can make your reading count.
Spell out each number.

1. _____-Eyed Cat

2. Goody _____-Shoes

3. The _____ Billy Goats Gruff

4. _____ Days

5. Across _____ Aprils

6. The _____ Swans

7. The _____ Dwarfs

8. _____ Is Enough

9. The _____ Tailors

10. _____ O'Clock Scholar

Now list the numbers in order.

____ ____ ____ ____ ____ ____ ____ ____ ____ ____

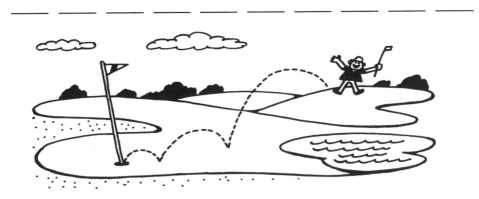

THIS IS CALLED A HOLE IN _____ .

1–60 REDS ARE READ

Many good books or characters make us see red. How many book titles or characters can you fill in with the color of red (or scarlet) in their titles? Be sure to use capital letters at the beginning of the words.

1. Little _____ Riding Hood

2. Where the _____ Fern Grows

3. The Little _____ Hen

4. The _____ Pimpernel

5. The _____ Badge of Courage

6. The Hunt for _____ October

7. The _____ Letter

8. The Ransom of _____ Chief

9. The Thin _____ Line

10. A Proud Taste for _____ and Miniver

11. Outlaw _____

12. The _____ Pony

13. Big _____

14. Irish _____

15. _____ (t) O'Hara

1–61 WHAT CHARACTER AM I?

Pick out a character from a popular book. Write down clues about yourself. When it is your turn, read one clue at a time and let your classmates guess who you are. See if you can make them think, but still guess who you are in five clues or less.

Example:

CLUE #1   I am a baby animal.

CLUE #2   There are three of us in the story.

CLUE #3   A blond girl visits our house.

CLUE #4   We left our porridge on the table.

CLUE #5   I cry because my chair gets broken.

What character am I? Baby Bear in <u>Goldilocks and the Three Bears</u>

CLUE #1_____

_____

CLUE #2_____

_____

CLUE #3_____

_____

CLUE #4_____

_____

CLUE #5_____

_____

MY CHARACTER IS _____

_____

1–62 ANIMAL CHARACTERS OUTLINE

Below are some favorite animal characters from stories you probably have read. Write the characters in ALPHABETICAL ORDER under the proper headings in the outline below.

1. Black Beauty
2. Gentle Ben
3. Puss-in-Boots
4. White Fang
5. Garfield
6. Flicka
7. Paddington
8. Winnie-the-Pooh

9. Misty
10. Big Red
11. Ribsy
12. Cat in the Hat
13. Stormy
14. Socks
15. Berenstain
16. Clifford

I. DOGS

A._____

B._____

C._____

D. _____

II. BEARS

A._____

B._____

C._____

D. _____

III. CATS

A._____

B._____

C._____

D. _____

IV. HORSES

A._____

B._____

C._____

D. _____

1–63 COLOR THE RHYME

1. Color or shade in words that rhyme with **and**.

2. Color or shade in words that rhyme with **mad**.

3. Color or shade in words that rhyme with **like**.

4. What does the picture remind you of? _____

cat	best	bike	nose	rope
fast	kite	hand	feet	pole
sand	had	bad	pike	sad
let	ran	hike	gave	feel
must	came	band	take	made

1–64 EASY RHYMING PAIRS

Each pair of answers will rhyme. Example: <u>pair</u> and <u>rare</u> rhyme. Look at the clues to find the rhyming pairs.

1. a number _____

   repair _____

2. direction _____

   exam _____

3. breakfast food _____

   walk on these _____

4. a season _____

   ties knots _____

5. you sit in _____

   two _____

6. small cats _____

   wear on hands _____

7. not tight _____

   white fowl _____

8. write with _____

   grown boys _____

© 1996 by The Center for Applied Research in Education

1–65 RHYME TIME WORD SEARCH

Rhymed words have endings that sound the same. Search for and circle (enclose) words that rhyme with POP ROCK BAND. Spell correctly all words in the word search puzzle that rhyme with any of these three words and put them in the proper columns below.

The rhyming words may go up, down, across, or diagonally. The letters of rhyming words may go forward or backward in the puzzle. <u>Letters</u> may overlap, but a whole word won't count if it is entirely inside another word.

H	A	V	E	M	P	A	D	D	N	A	R	G
A	D	D	C	O	T	N	N	F	A	T	C	L
N	N	A	R	P	A	A	R	L	T	O	O	O
D	A	D	O	L	S	O	H	O	P	M	L	O
S	T	O	P	I	C	O	P	C	L	O	C	K
I	S	A	C	K	O	O	C	K	C	C	A	N
S	T	R	A	N	D	O	C	K	U	K	N	O

POP

1. _____

2. _____

3. _____

4. _____

5. _____

6. _____

7. _____

ROCK

1. _____

2. _____

3. _____

4. _____

5. _____

6. _____

7. _____

BAND

1. _____

2. _____

3. _____

4. _____

5. _____

6. _____

7. _____

1–66
DO YOU UNDERSTAND THE DICTIONARY?

These sentences are written using the pronunciation guide for words from the dictionary. See if you can decipher the message and do what it says.

Kăn ū rēd ŧhēz wûrdz ū'zǐng dǐk 'shə nĕr' ē sǐm' bəlz?

Ĭt ĭz gŏod prăk' tǐs tōo trī ǐt. Kŏ' pē ŧhə rēl wûrdz

ŏn ŧhə līnz bǐ lō!

_____

_____

_____

_____

_____

_____

_____

_____

_____

_____

© 1996 by The Center for Applied Research in Education

1–67 FICTION VERSUS NONFICTION

Fiction is made up (fantasy); nonfiction is NOT made up (fact). Circle the letter at the end of the FICTION sentence in each pair. Write the letters on the line below. Then unscramble the letters to form a word that will tell you how well you did.

1. The monster grabbed the mouse and ate it. (R)

   The cat grabbed the mouse and ate it. (B)

2. The queen bee was very little. (C)

   The fairy queen was very little. (T)

3. The boys were quiet as elves. (V)

   The elves were quiet as boys. (E)

4. The girls flew away on a magic carpet. (G)

   The girls performed magic on the carpet. (O)

5. Jack climbed the beanstalk high into the sky. (A)

   The eagles flew high into the sky. (D)

Write the letters of the fiction sentences here.

_____

Unscramble the letters to form a five-letter word that tells how well you sorted out fiction from nonfiction.

_____

Name _____

1–68 PROVERB NIT-PICKING

Follow the directions for each set of five proverbs.

A penny saved is a penny earned.
A rotten apple spoils the barrel.
All that glitters is not gold.
Beauty is only skin deep.
Don't give up the ship.

1. Subtract the number of <u>o</u>'s from the number of <u>a</u>'s.   _____
2. Add the number of syllables in the proverb with the least syllables
   to the answer above.   _____

Experience is the best teacher.
Health is better than wealth.
Honesty is the best policy.
If the shoe fits, put it on.
Misery loves company.

3. How many syllables in each of the two proverbs that have the most   _____
   syllables?
4. How many <u>o</u>'s are there in this set?   _____

Talk is cheap.
Silence is golden.
Opposites attract.
Overcome evil with good.
A stitch in time saves nine.

5. Count the total number of words in this set.   _____

6. Subtract the number of four-letter words from the answer above.   _____

Waste not, want not.
Let sleeping dogs lie.
Look before you leap.
Don't judge a book by its cover.
Handsome is as handsome does.

7. Subtract the number of words starting with <u>h</u> from the number of   _____
   words starting with <u>l</u>.
8. How many different words are repeated?   _____

Substitute your answers in the questions below. Are you right?

Answer 1 + Answer 2 = Answer 3 + Answer 4 – 2.

Answer 5 – Answer 6 = Answer 7 + Answer 8 + 2.

1–69 DICTIONARY GUIDE WORDS RACE

To the Teacher: Divide students into four rows. Rows 1 and 2 make one team; rows 3 and 4, the other. Place four identical dictionaries equi-distant from both teams (on a table in front of the room works well). Put words and blanks on the chalkboard as shown at the bottom of the page. Match the number of words in the column to the numbers of players in the row.

Number of Players: Entire class

How to Play: First players in each row go to their respective dictionaries and look up first entry words as shown on chalkboard. First player in row 1 writes *top-of-page* guide word in blank to the left of first word; first player in row 2 writes *last-word-on-page* guide word to the right of first word. Likewise, first player in row 3 writes *top-of-page* guide word in blank to the left of *his or her* first word; first player in row 4 writes *last-word-on-page* guide word to the right of the same word as his or her teammate.

No player can begin looking up a word until the previous player in his or her row has returned and been seated. Players are encouraged to hurry, but cannot turn pages so fast that they damage the dictionaries. Guide words must be spelled correctly or the team forfeits win. First team to finish wins.

Rationale: This game assists students in using guide words, instead of looking through entry words at random, as is common. It encourages them to be efficient and fast. Words chosen are of equal difficulty and similar beginning letters, so lists are fair to each team. Different lists prevent copying from other team.

Modification: This can be an individual activity (give list to each student), but the game is more fun.

ROW 1 GUIDE WORD	ENTRY WORD	ROW 2 GUIDE WORD	ROW 3 GUIDE WORD	ENTRY WORD	ROW 4 GUIDE WORD
_____	major	_____	_____	minor	_____
_____	pepper	_____	_____	popper	_____
_____	large	_____	_____	small	_____
_____	dog	_____	_____	cat	_____
_____	football	_____	_____	handball	_____
_____	boy	_____	_____	lad	_____
_____	goat	_____	_____	boat	_____
_____	smart	_____	_____	great	_____
_____	cot	_____	_____	dig	_____

1–70 ACROSS THE BOARD: CONSONANTS AND END CLUSTERS

To the Teacher: More children can play if you run off additional copies of the ACROSS THE BOARD game board and sets of SELECTED CONSONANT SQUARES (one set of 16 consonants B-V for every two players). The letters should be run off on tagboard or plastic overhead transparency material, then cut into small squares along the lines. It is helpful to keep letter sets in small plastic sandwich bags so you can see through to see what you have.

If students have a dispute over whether or not a word is actual, the room dictionary (or you, if you prefer) can be the final source.

Number of Players: Groups of 2 players each

Materials Needed:
- ACROSS THE BOARD game board (two pages attached so players starting on either side of the board will have identical cluster possibilities)
- SELECTED CONSONANT SQUARES (1 set B-V for every 2 players)
- Spinner

How to Play: Each player draws five consonants from the face-down assortment of 16 consonants. One player begins along the far left of the board. The other player begins along the far right of the board.

To begin, both players position their consonants in squares in the first column *on their side* of the board so that each consonant and the cluster make a word. Each player takes a turn. A turn consists of spinning the spinner to determine how many total spaces you may move your consonant. A player may move one consonant the total amount of the spin, or several consonants partial amounts, adding up to the total of the spin. A player may LAND only on a space that forms a word with the consonant. The player may move forward or sideways, but not backward or diagonally.

Players may "jump" an occupied square, but must count it as one of their total moves from the spinner. If they cannot move their total number of spaces, they forfeit them all. It then becomes the other player's turn.

If a consonant gets "stuck" with no way out to make a word, players may draw a new consonant from the pile, and put their old consonant face-down on the table. Their new consonant must be placed where the former consonant was on the board and this counts as the turn. (Player may not spin this turn.)

The object of the game is to get all five consonants to the other side of the board (in the opposite column from where the player started) so that they make words, and to do it before their opponent does.

© 1996 by The Center for Applied Research in Education

SELECTED CONSONANT SQUARES

B	L
C	M
D	N
F	P
G	R
H	S
J	T
K	V

B	L
C	M
D	N
F	P
G	R
H	S
J	T
K	V

B	L
C	M
D	N
F	P
G	R
H	S
J	T
K	V

B	L
C	M
D	N
F	P
G	R
H	S
J	T
K	V

B	L
C	M
D	N
F	P
G	R
H	S
J	T
K	V

B	L
C	M
D	N
F	P
G	R
H	S
J	T
K	V

B	L
C	M
D	N
F	P
G	R
H	S
J	T
K	V

B	L
C	M
D	N
F	P
G	R
H	S
J	T
K	V

ACROSS THE BOARD GAME BOARD
(LEFT SIDE—ATTACH TO NEXT SHEET)

AN	ANE	IN	INE
ET	EST	EE	ACE
AM	AME	IN	OAL
AR	ARE	OW	AND
AT	ATE	AB	ICK
IT	ITE	EN	ICE
UT	UTE	UM	ALE
OT	OON	OP	AIN

ACROSS THE BOARD GAME BOARD
(RIGHT SIDE—ATTACH TO PREVIOUS SHEET)

INE	IN	ANE	AN
ACE	EE	EST	ET
OAL	IN	AME	AM
AND	OW	ARE	AR
ICK	AB	ATE	AT
ICE	EN	ITE	IT
ALE	UM	UTE	UT
AIN	OP	OON	OT

1–71 WHAT DID I WRITE?

To the Teacher: Run off one WHAT DID I WRITE? GAME BOARD for each group of four or fewer players. Run off the 8 game cards on tagboard. Laminate, if possible. Emphasize that fiction books are grouped together alphabetically by author on the library shelves. (If your picture books are separate, point this out, too.)

Number of Players: 2–4

Materials Needed:

- WHAT DID I WRITE? game board
- WHAT DID I WRITE? cards
- 1 marker for each player

How to Play: Draw an author card. Name books or stories by the author. Turn the card over to see if you are correct. Put the card on the bottom of the pack. Advance the number of spaces that equals the number of books named by that author. (Some titles are on the back of the card, but there is not room for them all and authors are constantly writing, so if all players agree that the title given is by that author, it counts in the number of spaces moved forward.) The first person to reach the center (GOAL) is the winner.

Rationale: It is hoped that by hearing old favorites over and over, the authors' names will stick in the students' minds. This game should help students find additional books by these famous authors more easily as they see the correct spellings of their names repeatedly while playing the game.

Modifications: Updated cards with other titles and authors you wish to have students learn can be added and/or substituted as desired.

WHAT DID I WRITE? GAME BOARD

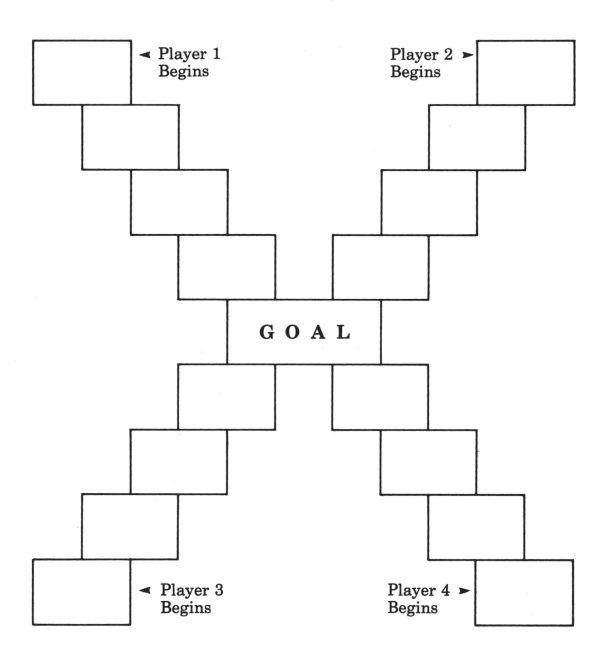

WHAT DID I WRITE? CARDS
(FRONT)

JUDITH VIORST	**MAURICE SENDAK**
BEVERLY CLEARY	**WANDA GAG**
SHEL SILVERSTEIN	**EZRA JACK KEATS**
MERCER MAYER	**DR. SEUSS**

WHAT DID I WRITE? CARDS
(BACK)

<u>Alexander and the Terrible Horrible</u> <u>No Good Very Bad Day</u> <u>Freckle Juice</u> <u>The Pain and the Great One</u> <u>Try It Again, Sam</u> <u>Rosie and Michael</u> <u>I'll Fix Anthony</u> <u>Sunday Morning</u>	<u>Where the Wild Things Are</u> <u>One Was Johnny: A Counting Book</u> <u>Alligators All Around</u> <u>Pierre</u> <u>Apt. 3–G</u>
<u>The Mouse and the Motorcycle</u> <u>Ramona the Pest</u> <u>Otis Spofford</u> <u>Henry and Beezus</u> <u>Ribsy</u> <u>Ralph S. Mouse</u> <u>Henry Huggins</u>	<u>Millions of Cats</u> <u>The ABC Bunny</u>
<u>A Giraffe and a Half</u> <u>Lafcadio, the Lion Who Shot Back</u> <u>Where the Sidewalk Ends</u> <u>The Giving Tree</u> <u>A Light in the Attic</u>	<u>Whistle for Willie</u> <u>Peter's Chair</u> <u>Clementine's Cactus</u> <u>Over in the Meadow</u> <u>The Snowy Day</u> <u>Louie</u> <u>The Trip</u>
<u>A Boy, a Dog, and a Frog</u> <u>What Do You Do With a Kangaroo</u> <u>Applelard and Liverwurst</u> <u>Lisa Lou and the Yellow Belly Swamp</u> <u>There's a Nightmare in My Closet</u> <u>Just Me and My Dad</u> <u>If I Had . . .</u>	<u>Green Eggs and Ham</u> <u>The Cat in the Hat</u> <u>If I Ran the Zoo</u> <u>I Am Not Going to Get Up Today</u> <u>Horton Hatches an Egg</u>

1–72. FINDING FICTION

To the Teacher: This game can be used for finding books in the Easy Books section or the General Fiction section of the library.

Number of Players: Entire class

Materials Needed:
- Library
- ALPHABET CARDS
- Construction paper or other indicators to put in shelves where book is removed

How to Play: Pass out one letter to each student. Each player finds a book on the library shelves that corresponds to their letter and places a marker on the shelves to indicate where the book was. This can be done singly, in twos, threes, half a class, or the whole class at once.

Upon returning to their seats or tables, each student exchanges his or her book and alphabet letter with another student. Then students return the traded, different book to the shelves using the traded alphabet letter as a clue. They should remove the marker paper from the shelves as they return the book.

Rationale: This is not a contest or win-lose game—just a practice for novice students. The teacher should help as needed to familiarize children with finding fiction on the shelves.

Modification: If the students are very naive about the library, you can skip the step of trading the books and markers, and just let the children return the same book that they found on the shelf. This often builds confidence until they are ready to be more independent.

1–73 ALPHABET SONG

The following song has taken many forms over the years. It is sung to the tune of "Twinkle, Twinkle, Little Star," and is a very effective way of teaching the alphabet to younger children.

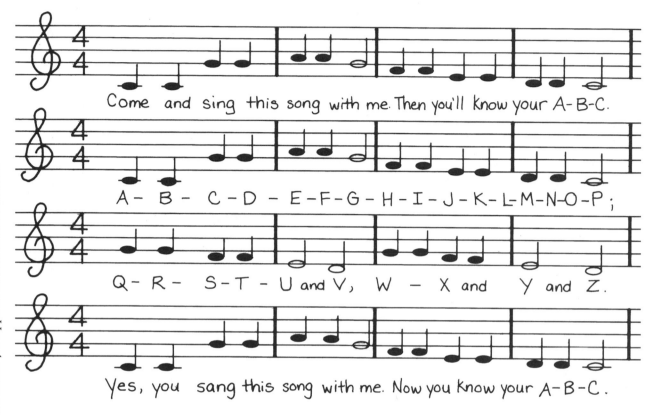

For older students or faster learners, try it backwards. See the third-line modification.

COME AND SING THIS SONG WITH ME. THEN YOU'LL KNOW YOUR ABC. THIS WILL BE QUITE FUN, YOU SEE, SINGING BACKWARD ABC. ZYX, WV, UTS and RQP; ONM and LKJ, IHGFED (they love to rush this together!), C . . . B . . . A (slowly, for a big finish.).

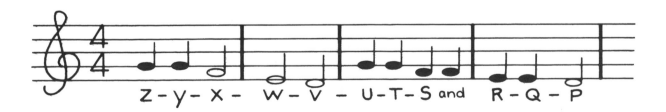

1–74 ALPHABET GAME

To the Teacher: Give every student a different alphabet card. One student is called upon to begin (student with middle letter is best). If you have more than 26 students, the students without cards can be the "audience." When students get to <u>Z</u>, the letter coming after will be considered to be <u>A</u>.

Number of Players: Entire class

Materials Needed:
- ALPHABET CARDS

How to Play:

Student #1: Comes to front of the room and displays the alphabet card, saying, "I'm an <u>M</u>. Who comes after me?"

Student with <u>N</u>: Positions self on stage right of Student #1, saying, "I do. I'm an <u>N</u>. Who comes after me?"

Game continues until all letters are in proper order around the room. Students then should each say their letter in order while displaying their alphabet card.

Rationale: It is important that students physically arrange themselves in proper order so that the kinesthetic experience keeps them interested and helps them remember the alphabet. It is also imperative that the alphabet be repeated in total at the end for reinforcement of learning and for fuller participation.

Modifications (harder): Have students ask, "Who comes before me?" Another variation (requiring even more thought): Have students ask either question ("Who comes before me?" or "Who comes after me?") at their discretion.

ALPHABET CARDS

A	A
E	E
I	I
O	O

ALPHABET CARDS (CONTINUED)

U	U
B	C
D	F
G	H

ALPHABET CARDS (CONTINUED)

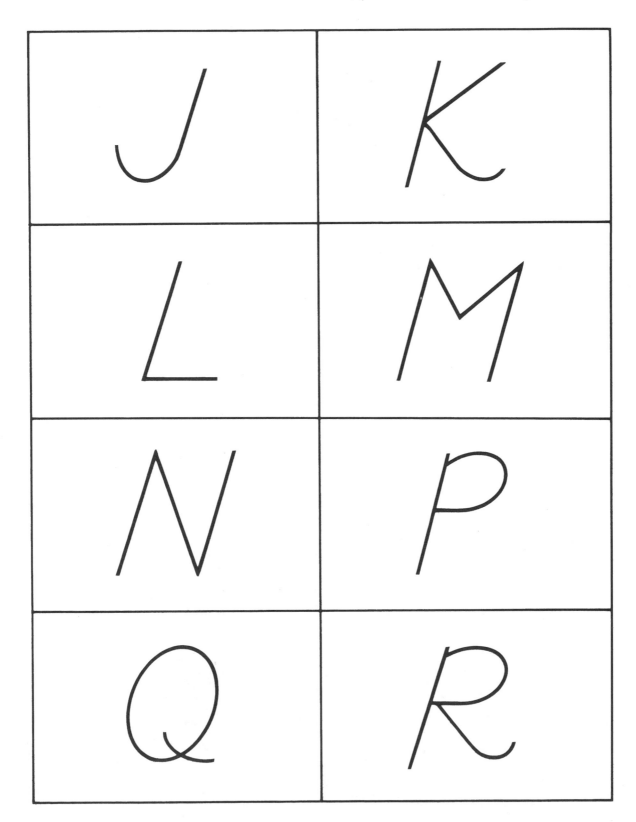

ALPHABET CARDS (CONTINUED)

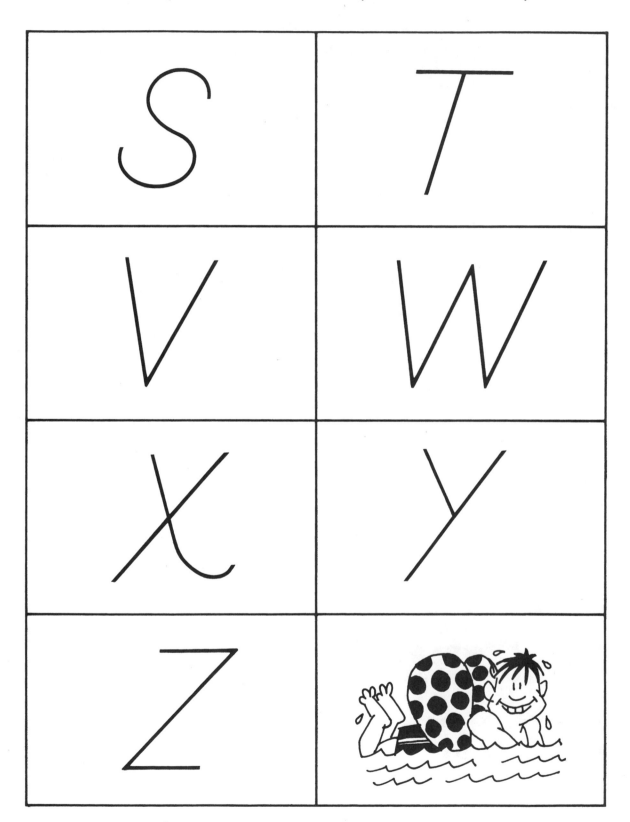

1–75 WORD GAME I

To the Teacher: Materials needed for these three games are the same.

Number of Players: 2

Materials Needed:
- Consonant cards from ALPHABET CARDS
- PHONOGRAM CARDS

How to Play: Mix both sets of cards. Deal out all cards, half to each player. Place the cards face down in a pack in front of you. Both players count together softly, saying "1, 2," and at the count of "3," both players turn over their top card from their own pack. See if a word is formed. If so, players say it <u>fast</u>. The first one to say the word captures both cards. (Put them on the bottom of the pack.) If a player says a word that is incorrect, the opposing player gets the cards. The player who has the most cards at the end of the time limit (or who has captured all the cards) is the winner.

1–76 WORD GAME II

Number of Players: 2–4

How to Play: Mix both sets of cards. Deal each player seven cards, put one card face up to start a discard pile, and leave the rest upside down in a "draw" pack. At each turn, draw a card from the "draw" pack or discard pile, lay down any cards making words, and discard a card on the discard pile. The object of the game is to get rid of all your cards. The first person to do so is the winner.

Modification: Older students may want to play several games and score points: 5 points for getting rid of all cards first; 2 points for each word formed; –1 point per card left in hand when someone else gets rid of all cards.

1–77 WORD GAME III

Number of Players: 2–4

How to Play: Put the single consonant cards in one container, the PHONOGRAM CARDS in the other. Shake the containers before each turn. Draw one card from each container. If the cards form a word and the player can say it, the player gets a point. If they don't form a word, the next player takes a turn. The first player to reach 10 points wins.

PHONOGRAM CARDS

ab	**ade**
ace	**ag**
ack	**ake**
ad	**am**

ame	**ang**
an	**ank**
ane	**ap**
and	**ape**

ar	**aw**
ash	**ay**
at	**ed**
ate	**ell**

en	ice
ent	ick
est	id
et	ide

PHONOGRAM CARDS (CONTINUED)

ig	**in**
ing	**ip**
ink	**ish**
im	**it**

ob	**old**
ock	**ong**
od	**op**
og	**ot**

ub	**um**
ud	**un**
uff	**ush**
ug	**ut**

Section Two

SPELLING AND VOCABULARY

2–1 COLOR STRETCH

Put the colors in the puzzle spaces reading across. (No words will be formed reading up and down!)

A s-t-r-e-t-c-h-e-d space needs only one letter stretched out and will be used in more than one word. The words in the COLOR BANK show how many letters are in each color to help you fill in the puzzle.

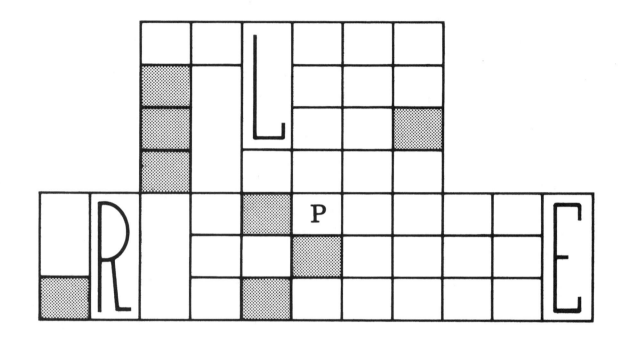

COLOR BANK

3 LETTERS	5 LETTERS	6 LETTERS
red	black	orange
	brown	purple
4 LETTERS	green	yellow
	white	
blue		
grey		

2–2 MIX AND MATCH COLORS

The primary colors are red, yellow, and blue. Most other colors are mixtures of these. See if you can mix and match them correctly. Use the COLOR BANK to help you.

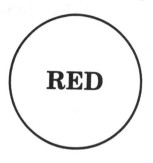  

1. The word in the first circle is _____.

2. The word in the middle circle is_____.

3. The word in the last circle is _____.

Using the bottom of this paper, mix crayon or pencil colors to see what colors you make. If you use crayon, color very lightly. Then answer the next three questions. The COLOR BANK will help you spell your answers right.

4. RED and YELLOW mixed become _____.

5. YELLOW and BLUE mixed become _____.

6. RED and BLUE mixed become _____.

COLOR BANK:

PURPLE   YELLOW   RED   ORANGE   GREEN   BLUE

Use the space below to mix your colors.

Name _____

2–3 SHAPE WORDS

Fill in the word from the SHAPE BANK that relates to the shapes of the items listed after each number.

1. ring   hoop   _____

2. brick   newspaper   _____

3. pyramid   tepee   _____

4. egg   human eye   _____

5. chessboard   baby block   _____

In the boxes below, draw each shape and label it.

SHAPE BANK:

square
triangle
oval
circle
rectangle

2–4 DEAR TALE OR DEER TAIL?

See how many homonyms you can spell correctly. Choose the best word from each pair at the bottom of the page, and write it in the box that has the same number. Is this about a deer tail, or is it just a dear tale?

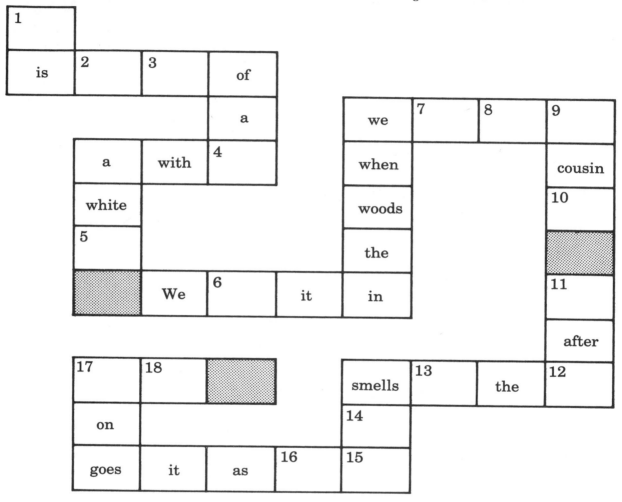

1. Hear, Here
2. our, hour
3. tale, tail
4. dear, deer
5. tale, tail
6. hear, here

7. meet, meat
8. our, hour
9. dear, deer
10. their, there
11. Our, Hour
12. our, hour

13. dear, deer
14. for, four
15. our, hour
16. scent, sent
17. its, it's
18. weigh, way

HINT: Words that sound alike but have different meanings (and usually different spellings) are called <u>homophones</u>.

© 1996 by The Center for Applied Research in Education

Name _____

2–5 BARE/BEAR PUZZLE

<u>Bare</u> and <u>bear</u> are homonyms. That is, they are words that sound alike but have different meanings. In fact, both these words have several meanings. See how many you can fit correctly into the puzzle.

ACROSS

1. Paddington _____
2. Mother Hubbard's cupboard
3. _____ly alive
4. _____ your legs in shorts
5. _____ your innermost secrets
6. The right to _____ arms
7. Someone Goldilocks visited
8. Panda _____
9. Can you _____ the news?

DOWN

1. Pooh _____
2. Some trees _____ fruit
3. To _____ up under a weight
5. Care _____
6. A tree without leaves
7. A dog might _____ his teeth
8. Do it with your _____ hands

101

2–6 DROP-A-LETTER SOUND-ALIKES

Drop a letter from the front OR back of each word. You will get a new word that is called a <u>homonym</u>. Homonyms are words that sound alike, but have different meanings.

1. bee

    _____

2. knew

    _____

3. hour

    _____

4. wee

    _____

5. ore

    _____

6. too

    _____

7. knot

    _____

8. knight

    _____

© 1996 by The Center for Applied Research in Education

2–7 HOMONYMS THE EASY WAY

Drop a letter from the front OR back of each underlined word to form a different word that sounds exactly like it (a homonym). Put the new word on the line provided.

1. After so many calls, Morgan had to <u>wring</u> her hands when she heard

   the phone _____ again.

2. In <u>Maine</u> one of the _____ attractions is Bar Harbor.

3. The <u>whole</u> golf team cheered when Max made a _____
   in one.

4. The deep <u>burrow</u> made the _____ lose his footing
   and stumble.

5. Just as Juan was about to <u>wrap</u> the presents, he heard a loud

   _____ at the door.

6. Frank had already said <u>bye</u> to his friends _____ the
   time he realized he had forgotten to thank them for coming.

7. Maria <u>knew</u> there was no way she would have a _____
   dress in time for the party.

8. My parents tried to <u>add</u> up the savings from all the coupons in the

   _____ to see how much they could save.

9. Chris liked the <u>scent</u> of the perfume, but she needed one more

   _____ to pay for it.

10. The farmer had to <u>sow</u> his seeds early in the year _____
    he would have a good harvest in the fall.

Name _____

2–8 "B" WORDS THAT LEAD A DOUBLE LIFE

Each of these words has at least two meanings. One meaning is shown by a clue in the first column. Think of another life the word leads. Then put each word where it makes most sense. The spellings will stay the same. Cross out the words in the HOMOGRAPH BANK as you use them.

1. ten-minute <u>break</u>

2. hair <u>brush</u>

3. <u>bore</u> a hole

4. infected <u>boil</u>

5. dog's <u>bark</u>

6. <u>bear</u> the pain

7. pay the <u>bill</u>

8. winged <u>bat</u>

9. <u>box</u> his ears

10. rubber <u>band</u>

11. call her <u>bluff</u>

12. <u>bowl</u> on Saturday

a. five-piece _____

b. _____ your guests

c. four-sided _____

d. duck's _____

e. baseball _____

f. _____ the window

g. grizzly _____

h. spoon and _____

i. high _____

j. clearing the _____

k. tree's _____

l. _____ the potatoes

HOMOGRAPH BANK			
break	bore	bluff	boil
brush	bark	bowl	bat
bear	band	bill	box

104

2–9 HOMOGRAPHS

Homographs are words that are spelled the same, but have different meanings and origins. Circle any <u>five</u> words below. Use these words in a story so that each word has at least two meanings. Underline the homographs in your story. You should have ten underlined words.

chop	fan	lap	palm	second
clip	fly	lean	pen	sock
colon	hide	left	prune	spell
counter	hold	list	pupil	stalk
fair	jam	loaf	school	story

_____

_____

_____

_____

_____

_____

_____

_____

_____

_____

_____

_____

2–10 REVERSE IT

These letters from first- and second-grade spelling lists all spell one word forward and a different word when reversed. Write the new words in the blanks.

1. net _____

2. was _____

3. not _____

4. pot _____

5. got _____

6. on _____

7. bus _____

8. but _____

9. tug _____

10. step _____

11. keep _____

12. pots _____

13. spot _____

14. eat _____

15. now _____

16. star _____

17. meat _____

18. bur _____

2–11 BACKWARD AND FORWARD SPELLING

Words that are spelled the same backward and forward are called <u>palindromes</u>. With the clues given, fill in the missing letters in the puzzle so that the words spell the same both ways.

1. | M | O | |

2. | | E | P |

3. | S | | S |

4. | | U | P |

5. | P | O | |

6. | E | Y | |

7. | | A | D |

8. | D | I | |

9. | N | | | N |

10. | | | O | T |

11. | P | E | | |

2–12 THE OTHER SIDE OF THE COIN

Imagine you turn over each coin. What would be the opposite word that might appear on the other side? Write the other side of the coin on the coins below.

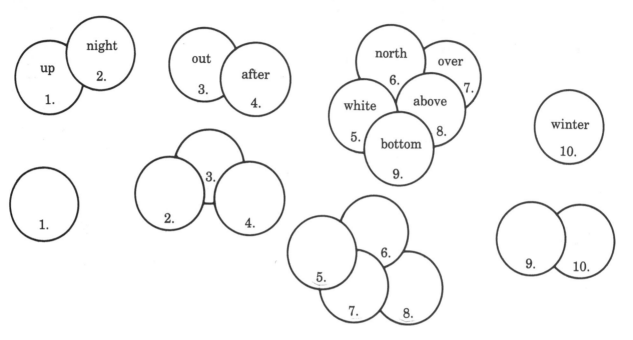

1. If all the coins were pennies, how much money would you have?

_____

2. If all the coins were nickels, how much money would you have?

_____

3. If all the coins were dimes, how much money would you have?

_____

© 1996 by The Center for Applied Research in Education

2–13 SAME AND OPPOSITE ANAGRAMS

This puzzle is filled with anagrams (words with scrambled letters). The letters at the top and side are the beginning letters of the words answering the clues.

   This is easier than it looks or sounds. Just cross out each letter as you use it. All the letters will be used.

	1 U	2 S	3 B	4 W	5 R	6 F	7 Q
1 A	C	N	O	E	H	L	I
2 D	L	I	E	N	C	R	T
3 E	G	H	I	A	T	O	E
4 C	W	T	N	M	O	D	L
5 L	A	O	Y	R	I	N	D
6 T	E	W	D	O	R	H	U
7 G	N	F	A	D	L	U	O

ACROSS (SAME)

1. not with anyone   A_____

2. one who dines   D_____

3. number   E_____

4. circus funnyman   C_____

5. woman   L_____

6. hurl   T_____

7. precious metal   G_____

DOWN (OPPOSITE)

1. opposite of aunt   U_____

2. opposite of hard   S_____

3. opposite of good   B_____

4. opposite of cool   W_____

5. opposite of poor   R_____

6. opposite of lost   F_____

7. opposite of loud   Q_____

2–14 END SOUNDS

See if you can figure out words that end with the letters shown. Use the definitions to help you.

WORDS	CLUES	WORDS	CLUES
1. _ _ _ _ a	snake	14. _ _ n	grown boy
2. _ _ b	taxi	15. _ _ _ _ o	car
3. _ _ _ c	for computer	16. _ _ _ p	boat
4. _ _ d	color	17. _ _ _ q	country
5. _ _ _ _ e	Native American tent	18. _ _ _ _ _ r	plays role
6. _ _ f	not on	19. _ _ _ _ s	map book
7. _ _ g	has foot	20. _ _ _ t	piece of
8. _ _ _ _ h	for teeth	21. _ _ _ _ _ u	short poem
9. _ _ _ _ i	excuse	22. _ _ v	race motor
10. _ j	disc jockey	23. _ _ _ w	cat sound
11. _ _ _ _ k	tells time	24. _ x	animal
12. _ _ _ l	goes with rod	25. _ _ y	unlocks doors
13. _ _ _ m	wander	26. _ _ _ z	kind of music

2–15 DO YOU LIKE ART?

All twelve words have <u>art</u> in them, though none of them relate to art. Use the clues and see how many you can figure out. Write the missing letters on the blanks.

WORDS		CLUES
1.	__ ART	never put before the horse
2.	__ ART	dash fast
3.	__ ART	piece
4.	__ ART	not sweet; kind of bitter
5.	__ ART	ugly growth
6.	__ __ ART	diagram
7.	__ __ ART	pumps blood in body
8.	__ __ ART	equals four cups
9.	__ __ ART	bright
10.	__ __ ART	begin
11.	__ ART __	our planet
12.	__ ART __	get-together

Name _____

2–16 RELATED WORDS

The letters in each box form a four-letter word. (Begin with the circled letter and go to the right, left, up, or down to find the word in each box.) Then write the words on the lines. The first and last word in each row is related to the middle word in that row.

1.
| o n | (b) a | e   m |
| w (s) | l   l | (g) a |
_____ _____

2.
| (n) e | o (b) | (c) a |
| o   t | o   k | e   s |
_____ _____

3.
| h (b) | o   m | e   t |
| t   a | o (r) | (m) a |
_____ _____

4.
| (h) u | u   b | a (s) |
| t   n | l (c) | d   o |
_____ _____

5.
| m   u | (t) r | (t) s |
| (p) l | e   e | o   p |
_____ _____

6.
| e (l) | d   i | w   o |
| k   a | e (s) | (s) h |
_____ _____

7.
| (l) i | e (t) | n   e |
| e   f | m   i | i (l) |
_____ _____

8.
| e   m | o   r | (s) p |
| (h) o | (w) k | h   o |
_____ _____

9.
| (d) o | w   n | h (s) |
| n   w | o (t) | i   p |
_____ _____

112

© 1996 by The Center for Applied Research in Education

2–17 COMPOUND WORDS

Put words from the WORD COMPOUND into the proper blocks so that every connected block makes a compound word reading down.

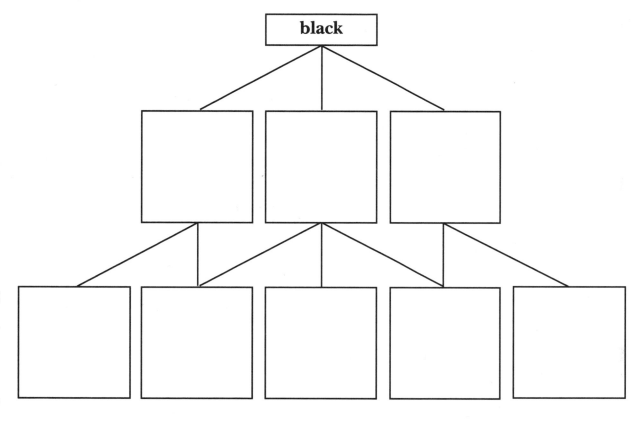

WORD COMPOUND

heavy	fit
out	bird
seed	side
top	house

2–18 COMPOUND TRAIN CARS

Compound words are longer words formed from two or more separate words. Use the words in the train station to hook the train cars together. Each group of three train cars will make two compound words. Use the word in the middle car as both the last part of the first word and the first part of the last word.

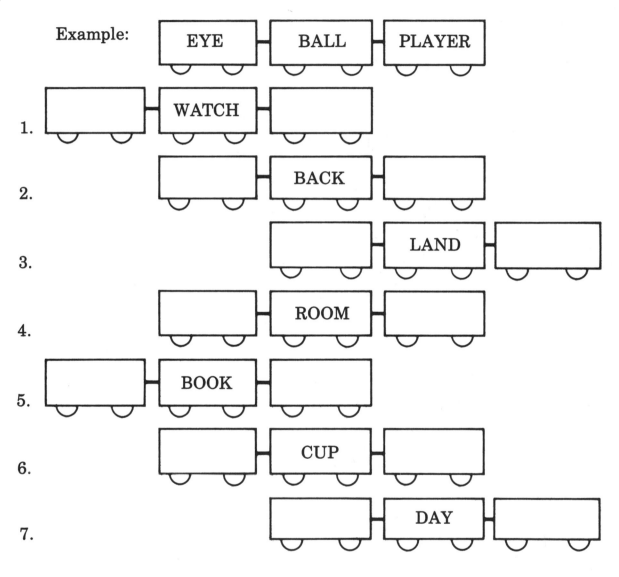

Example:

EYE — BALL — PLAYER

1. [ ] — WATCH — [ ]

2. [ ] — BACK — [ ]

3. [ ] — LAND — [ ]

4. [ ] — ROOM — [ ]

5. [ ] — BOOK — [ ]

6. [ ] — CUP — [ ]

7. [ ] — DAY — [ ]

TRAIN STATION

	LADY	BIRTH	
BREAK	NOTE	WOOD	BALL
DOG	TRACK	WRIST	MATE
BARE	BUTTER	KEEPER	CAKE

2–19 MISSING LINKS: ENDINGS

Use the MISSING LINKS BANK to fill in the missing letters in the necklace and on the blanks.

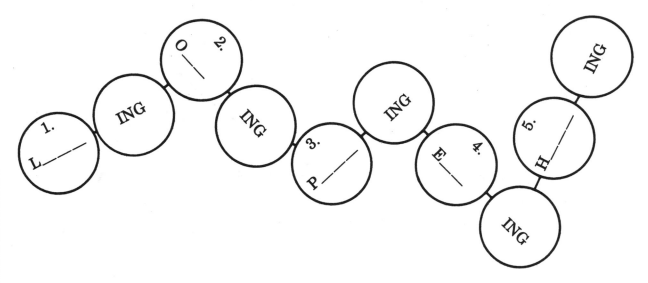

1. l __ __ __

2. o __ __

3. p __ __ __

4. e __ __

5. h __ __ __

MISSING LINKS BANK

own   end

hand   last   part

Now take the same words and add the ending <u>ed</u> to each.

6. _____

7. _____

8. _____

9. _____

10. _____

2–20 PREFIX AND SUFFIX KITE

Choose from PREFIXES AND SUFFIXES and add them to the root word <u>mix</u>. Put the new words with prefixes on the blanks in the kite. Put the new words with suffixes on the tail of the kite.

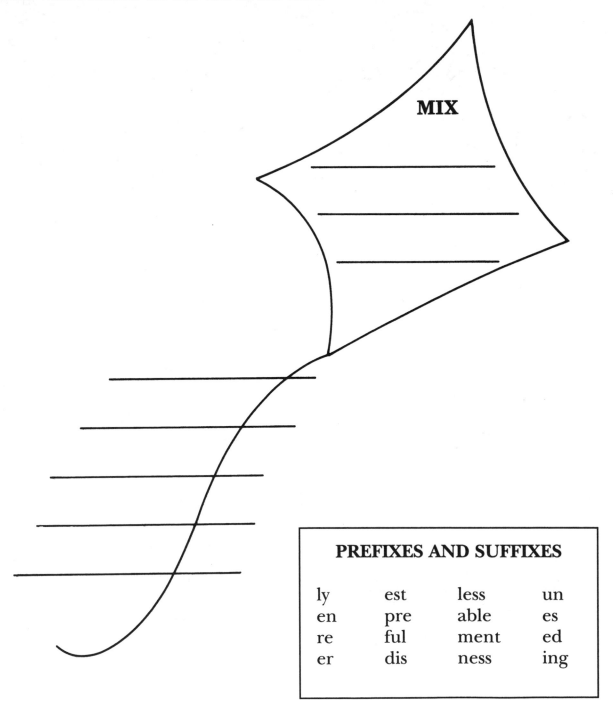

MIX

PREFIXES AND SUFFIXES

ly	est	less	un
en	pre	able	es
re	ful	ment	ed
er	dis	ness	ing

© 1996 by The Center for Applied Research in Education

2–21 WHAT LETTERS DO YOU NEED TO ADD?
(PART I)

Add the same letter to each word in a column to form new words. You will add a different letter to each column. It goes fast once you figure out the letter!

1. ____e	1. ____et	1. ____en	1. ____ox
2. ____ee	2. ____eg	2. ____et	2. ____un
3. ____ed	3. ____ot	3. ____ig	3. ____an
4. ____it	4. ____aw	4. ____an	4. ____og
5. ____ig	5. ____ow	5. ____op	5. ____ry
6. ____ug	6. ____ook	6. ____in	6. ____ly
7. ____us	7. ____ong	7. ____at	7. ____ar
8. ____ut	8. ____ake	8. ____lum	8. ____rog
9. ____est	9. ____ike	9. ____ole	9. ____ast
10. ____ike	10. ____eft	10. ____ond	10. ____our
11. ____ite	11. ____ine	11. ____ipe	11. ____arm
12. ____one	12. ____ost	12. ____art	12. ____eet

2–22 WHAT LETTERS DO YOU NEED TO ADD? (PART II)

Add the same letter to each word in a column to form new words. You will add a different letter to each column. It goes fast once you figure out the letter!

1. ____an	1. ____et	1. ____o	1. ____o
2. ____at	2. ____ob	2. ____op	2. ____et
3. ____ut	3. ____ug	3. ____ub	3. ____ot
4. ____ap	4. ____ab	4. ____ry	4. ____un
5. ____ot	5. ____ay	5. ____wo	5. ____row
6. ____up	6. ____ut	6. ____en	6. ____ive
7. ____ar	7. ____ar	7. ____ree	7. ____rey
8. ____ow	8. ____am	8. ____ake	8. ____ame
9. ____ame	9. ____ot	9. ____ime	9. ____ate
10. ____all	10. ____oke	10. ____alk	10. ____ave
11. ____lap	11. ____ump	11. ____ape	11. ____ood
12. ____oat	12. ____ust	12. ____old	12. ____irl

© 1996 by The Center for Applied Research in Education

2–23 WHAT LETTERS DO YOU NEED TO ADD?
(PART III)

Add the same letter to each word in a column to form new words. You will add a different letter to each column. It goes fast once you figure out the letter!

1. ___o	1. ___e	1. ___an	1. ___it
2. ___ad	2. ___ad	2. ___ed	2. ___ey
3. ___id	3. ___at	3. ___un	3. ___id
4. ___ot	4. ___as	4. ___ug	4. ___in
5. ___og	5. ___is	5. ___ing	5. ___iss
6. ___ay	6. ___im	6. ___ode	6. ___ind
7. ___ig	7. ___ot	7. ___oom	7. ___ick
8. ___ry	8. ___op	8. ___est	8. ___eep
9. ___ark	9. ___ug	9. ___ock	9. ___ite
10. ___ust	10. ___ike	10. ___ake	10. ___ilt
11. ___uck	11. ___ome	11. ___ide	11. ___ing
12. ___ish	12. ___ope	12. ___ope	12. ___itten

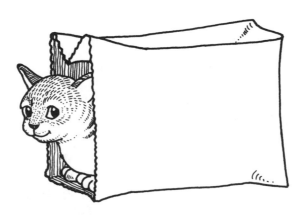

2–24 WHAT LETTERS DO YOU NEED TO ADD?
(PART IV)

Add the same letter to each word in a column to form new words. You will add a different letter to each column. It goes fast once you figure out the letter!

1. ____e	1. ____o	1. ____et	1. ____an
2. ____as	2. ____et	2. ____ea	2. ____et
3. ____eek	3. ____ot	3. ____un	3. ____om
4. ____alk	4. ____ow	4. ____ee	4. ____ay
5. ____ill	5. ____od	5. ____afe	5. ____op
6. ____ent	6. ____ew	6. ____oon	6. ____ap
7. ____ave	7. ____oon	7. ____eed	7. ____ud
8. ____ant	8. ____ine	8. ____lam	8. ____ust
9. ____ait	9. ____ame	9. ____ame	9. ____ade
10. ____ish	10. ____ose	10. ____ide	10. ____ine
11. ____ith	11. ____eed	11. ____ave	11. ____ilk
12. ____ell	12. ____ice	12. ____till	12. ____ule

Name _____

2–25 AS EASY AS 1-2-3

Follow the directions for each set using the WORD BANK to help you. Cross out the words in the WORD BANK as you use them. You will use each word once.

Set I

1. Add 1 letter to M and get <u>yourself</u>. _____

2. Add 2 letters to M and get <u>an adult male</u>. _____

3. Add 3 letters to M and get <u>more than a few</u>. _____

Set II

1. Add 1 letter to H and get <u>a greeting</u>. _____

2. Add 2 letters to H and get <u>opposite of "him."</u> _____

3. Add 3 letters to H and get <u>opposite of "low."</u> _____

4. Add 4 letters to H and get <u>a place to live</u>. _____

Set III

1. Add 1 letter to W and get <u>us</u>. _____

2. Add 2 letters to W and get <u>opposite of "peace."</u> _____

3. Add 3 letters to W and get <u>opposite of "play."</u> _____

4. Add 4 letters to W and get <u>wet stuff</u>. _____

5. Add 5 letters to W and get <u>past tense of "want."</u> _____

WORD BANK					
house	water	her	hi	many	work
wanted	man	me	we	high	war

121

2–26 JUST THREE-LETTER WORDS

See how many 3-letter words you can make by adding one different letter at the beginning.

at	**et**	**it**	**ot**	**ut**
_____	_____	_____	_____	_____
_____	_____	_____	_____	_____
_____	_____	_____	_____	_____
_____	_____	_____	_____	_____
_____	_____	_____	_____	_____
_____	_____	_____	_____	_____
_____	_____	_____	_____	_____
_____	_____	_____	_____	_____
_____	_____	_____	_____	_____

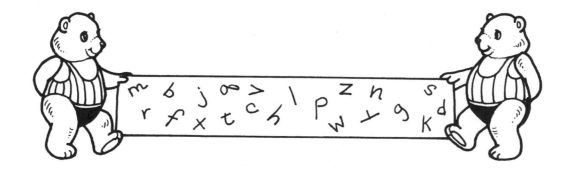

2–27 THREE-BAGGERS

Keep dropping the first or last letter until you have three words in all.

1. when

_____

_____

2. fork

_____

_____

3. bush

_____

_____

4. them

_____

_____

5. beef

_____

_____

6. took

_____

_____

7. good

_____

_____

8. done

_____

_____

9. does

_____

_____

10. small

_____

_____

11. week

_____

_____

12. been

_____

_____

13. fine

_____

_____

14. wind

_____

_____

2–28 DROPSY I

Drop the first letter each time and form a new word.

1. can

_____

2. bit

_____

3. hat

_____

4. the

_____

5. was

_____

6. ham

_____

7. bus

_____

8. his

_____

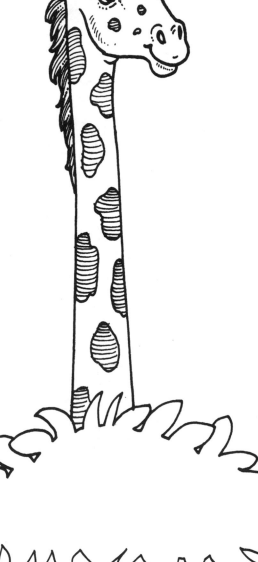

2–29 DROPSY II

Drop the last letter each time and form a new word.

1. seed

_____

2. feet

_____

3. note

_____

4. hope

_____

5. ride

_____

6. bite

_____

7. hide

_____

8. rode

_____

2–30 FOUR-BAGGERS

Keep dropping the first or last letter until you have four words in all. **Hint:** The last word for each MAY have one letter.

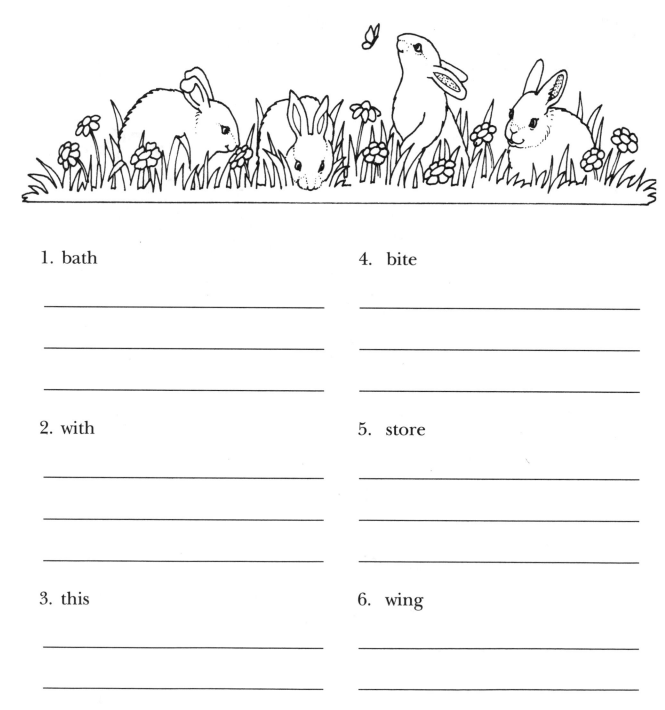

1. bath

_____

_____

_____

2. with

_____

_____

_____

3. this

_____

_____

_____

4. bite

_____

_____

_____

5. store

_____

_____

_____

6. wing

_____

_____

_____

Name _____

2–31 A FINE KETTLE OF FISH

Add or subtract one letter from each underlined word so that every word is spelled correctly and the sentences make sense.

        (1)   (2)   (3)   (4)   (5)   (6) (7) (8) (9)
The <u>mann</u> <u>waked</u> in <u>withe</u> his <u>basets</u> <u>ful</u>. "I <u>wil</u> <u>tel</u> <u>yu</u> <u>riht</u>

         (10)   (11)   (12) (13)   (14)
now," he <u>sid</u>, "I <u>frye</u> a <u>finne</u> <u>ketle</u> of <u>fishe</u>."

Put the correct words on the blanks below.

(1) _____   (8) _____

(2) _____   (9) _____

(3) _____   (10) _____

(4) _____   (11) _____

(5) _____   (12) _____

(6) _____   (13) _____

(7) _____   (14) _____

2–32 ANAGRAM LADDERS

An anagram is a word that spells another word when the letters are arranged in a new way. In this puzzle you need to add a letter as you go up each rung of the ladder and then arrange the letters in a different way to form a new word. You MUST rearrange letters EACH TIME or your word won't count! (Don't use words ending in <u>s</u>.)

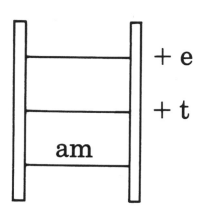

+ e

+ t

am

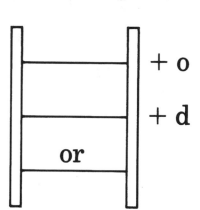

+ o

+ d

or

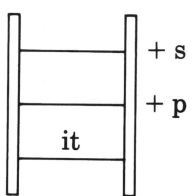

+ s

+ p

it

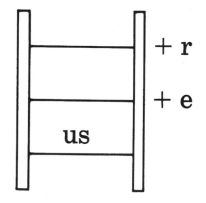

+ r

+ e

us

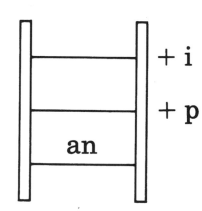

+ i

+ p

an

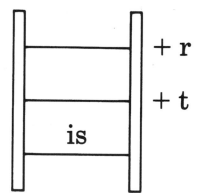

+ r

+ t

is

2–33 ADD-A-LETTER ANAGRAMS

Begin with the letter given. Add one letter at a time to form new words as you go down the pyramids. The letters can stay in order or be mixed up to form the new words.

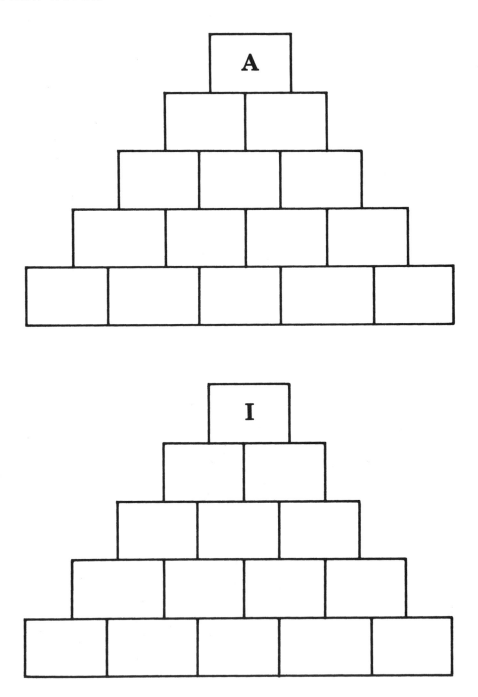

Name _____

2–34 LET'S GO TO THE CIRCUS

You might find all these things at the circus. There is just one problem. They have lost their vowels! See if you can find the right vowels so the circus can go on with the show. **HINT**: Vowels are <u>a</u>, <u>e</u>, <u>i</u>, <u>o</u>, and <u>u</u>.

1. C L ___ W N

2. P ___ ___ N ___ T S

3. ___ L ___ P H ___ N T

4. M ___ N K ___ Y

5. J ___ G G L ___ R

6. L ___ M ___ N ___ D ___

7. S ___ ___ L

8. ___ C R ___ B ___ T

9. B ___ L L ___ ___ N

10. C ___ T T ___ N   C ___ N D Y

11. L ___ ___ N   T ___ M ___ R

2–35 MISSING VOWEL PETALS

Begin at the top left petal and go clockwise on each flower to fill in the missing vowels (A, E, I, O, U). Write the names of the flowers on the lines.

1.

2.

3.

_____   _____   _____

4.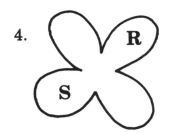

5.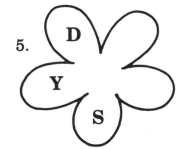

6.

_____   _____   _____

2–36 THE CASE OF THE MISSING VOWELS

Figure out the missing vowels in each group of words. Write the missing vowels in the blanks.

1. C __ N
   M __ N
   D __ D
   H __ D
   R __ N

2. M __ T
   M __ N
   G __ T
   Y __ S
   L __ T

3. D __ D
   H __ M
   B __ T
   B __ G
   S __ T

4. M __ M
   J __ B
   T __ P
   H __ T
   D __ T

5. S __ N
   N __ T
   H __ G
   R __ N
   C __ P

Write the five vowels here:

____ ____ ____ ____ ____

2–37 TWO BY FOUR

Building words is fun. Follow the directions to go from two- to four-letter words fast.

2 Letters	**3 Letters**	**4 Letters**
1. a t + m =	__ a t + e =	__ a t __
2. i n + p =	__ i n + e =	__ i n __
3. a n + c =	__ a n + e =	__ a n __
4. o n + d =	__ o n + e =	__ o n __
5. i t + k =	__ i t + e =	__ i t __
6. o r + f =	__ o r + e =	__ o r __
7. a m + t =	__ a m + e =	__ a m __

2–38 PLUS AND MINUS

The answers in this word puzzle all are related to one thing. Add and subtract letters to get the answers. Then write one word that all these words are related to at the bottom of the page.

HINT: You must add letters only at the end of the word!

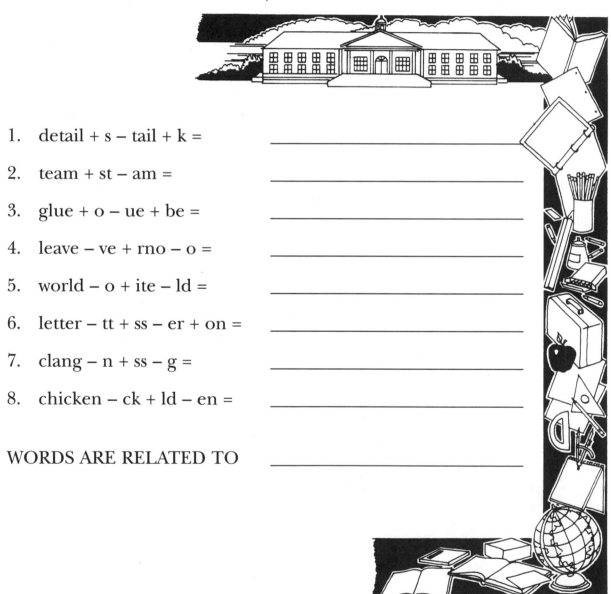

1.   detail + s − tail + k =   _____

2.   team + st − am =   _____

3.   glue + o − ue + be =   _____

4.   leave − ve + rno − o =   _____

5.   world − o + ite − ld =   _____

6.   letter − tt + ss − er + on =   _____

7.   clang − n + ss − g =   _____

8.   chicken − ck + ld − en =   _____

WORDS ARE RELATED TO   _____

2–39 WORD PLAY

It is fun to play with words just to see what can happen. Start at the bottom step. Change one letter in the word before you go up to the next rung. Can you change a boy to a bus? A girl to a bird? See if you can get to the top steps by putting the right words on the middle steps!

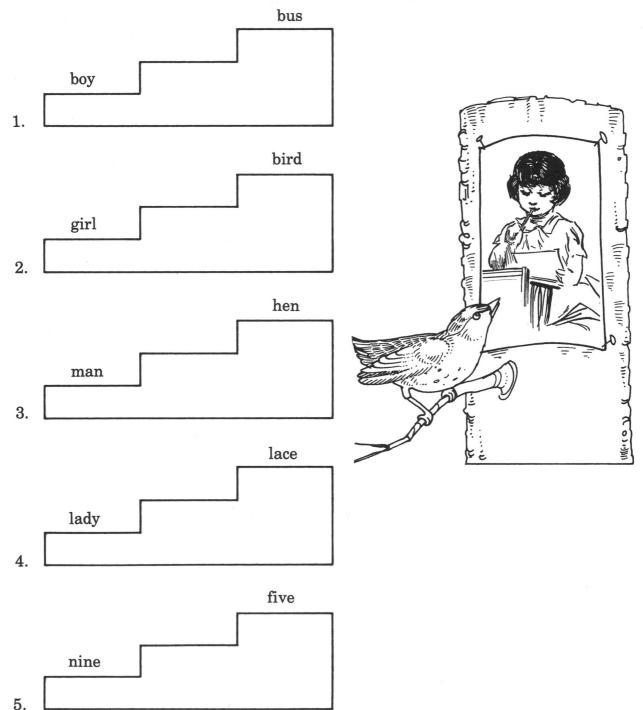

bus

boy

1.

bird

girl

2.

hen

man

3.

lace

lady

4.

five

nine

5.

2–40 CODE CLUES

Use the code clues to find the right words.

┌───┐
│ **CODE CLUES**   │
│ C = Letter is in right place.   │
│ X = Letter is in wrong place.   │
│ O = Letter is not in the word.   │
└───┘

1. for = oco
    yes = xoo
    tab = oox
    _____ = ccc

2. ten = xoo
    jar = oco
    ace = xxo
    _____ = ccc

3. did = cox
    not = oco
    get = xoo
    _____ = ccc

4. role = xoxo
    bite = ocoo
    grub = cxoo
    _____ = cccc

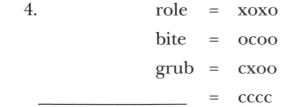

2–41 FIND THE COMMON LETTERS

Find the common letter in each set of words. The common letters will spell a word.

SET 1	SET 2	SET 3	SET 4	SET 5
badge	thirteen	oiled	peanuts	smart
along	trouble	forget	sandwich	secret
begin	yarn	where	extra	plate
_____	_____	_____	_____	_____

2–42 TWO-LETTER WORD BLOCKS

Circle ONE letter from each pair in the box so that two two-letter words are formed in both rows and columns. Write the four two-letter words you created for each set below.

Set I

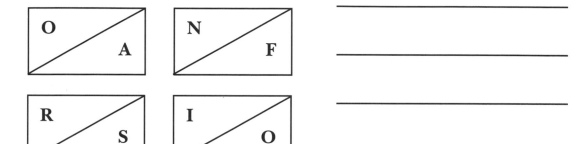

_____

_____

_____

_____

Set II

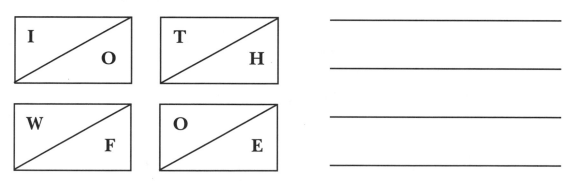

_____

_____

_____

_____

Name _____

2–43 LITTLE WORDS GET BIGGER

Add a letter and what do you have? Leave the letters in the same order, but add the new letter at the front or back.

1.

he
+ t
+ y

2.

is
+ h
+ t

3.

or
+ e
+ m

4.

he
+ m
+ t

5.

do
+ e
+ s

6.

he
+ n
+ t

7.

ad
+ e
+ m

8.

in
+ f
+ d

9.

an
+ m
+ y

10.

no
+ w
+ k

11.

to
+ o
+ k

12.

go
+ o
+ d

Name _____

2–44 LITTLE WORDS GET SMALLER

Remove a letter and what do you have? Leave the letters in the same order.

1. | T | H | A | T |
   −T
   −H

2. | H | A | N | D |
   −H
   −D

3. | W | I | T | H |
   −H
   −W

4. | T | H | I | S |
   −T
   −H

5. | B | E | E | N |
   −N
   −E

6. | T | H | A | N |
   −H
   −T

7. | T | R | A | M |
   −T
   −R

8. | W | H | E | N |
   −W
   −N

9. | H | E | R | E |
   −E
   −R

10. | D | O | W | N |
    −D
    −W

11. | O | N | C | E |
    −C
    −E

12. | Y | O | U | R |
    −Y
    −U

HAND
AND
AN

Name _____

2–45 SPIDER WEB SPELLING

See how many words you can form from this spider web. Follow the web in any direction, but do not go back over any part of the web during the same word. No one-letter words count. Score yourself as follows:

2-letter words: 2 points
3-letter words: 3 points
4-letter words: 4 points
5-letter words: 5 points

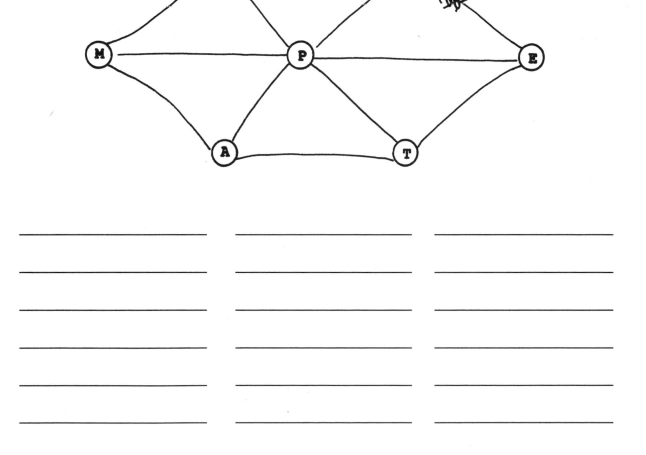

_____   _____   _____

_____   _____   _____

_____   _____   _____

_____   _____   _____

_____   _____   _____

_____   _____   _____

_____   _____   _____

Figure out your total points and put them here. _____

2–46 BACKWARDS SPELLING

See how well you know your spelling words. Begin at the right and go backwards to find words. There will be extra letters you will have to skip! Write the words on the blanks provided.

GRADE 3: tsalqvnalpsdnalwcpordncvtolpmdelslludxzffucpohcnulynoollab

1. _ _ _ _ _ _ _ _
2. _ _ _ _ _ _
3. _ _ _ _ _
4. _ _ _ _ _
5. _ _ _ _
6. _ _ _ _
7. _ _ _ _ _
8. _ _ _ _ _
9. _ _ _ _ _
10. _ _ _ _

GRADE 2: nafmndnahiatxenglniwlpucjkseodeetucgnol

1. _ _ _ _ _
2. _ _ _ _ _
3. _ _ _ _ _
4. _ _ _
5. _ _ _
6. _ _ _ _
7. _ _ _ _
8. _ _ _

GRADE 1: taaehtpqeraehsnnuoy

1. _ _ _
2. _ _ _
3. _ _ _
4. _ _ _
5. _ _

2–47 SPELLING MAZE

Follow the maze of misspelled words by shading in or coloring all incorrect words. On the lines below, write each word correctly.

aunt	buy	often	which	
among	hear	ferst	buzy	**BEGIN HERE**
been	peice	pritty	you	
blue	verry	toys	says	

END HERE

1. _____

2. _____

3. _____

4. _____

5. _____

2–48 DOUBLE <u>L</u> WORDS

All these words have <u>ll</u> in the middle. Each word has six letters. See how many you can figure out from the definitions. Hopefully, the circled letters will tell how you did.

1. __ __ l l __ __ (a type of large dog; Lassie)

2. ⃝ __ l l __ __ (what a horse does when he goes fast)

3. __ __ l l __ ⃝ (a worker in a bank who handles cash)

4. __ __ l l __ __ (a type of poem or song)

5. __ __ l l __ __ (one hundred pennies equals this)

6. __ __ l l⃝ __ (a murderer)

7. __ __ l l __ __ (the opposite of lead)

8. __ __ l l __ __ (flowers have it; sometimes causes allergy)

9. __ ⃝ l l __ __ (four quarts equal this)

10. __ __ l l __ ⃝ (the paper on which you cast your vote)

HOW DID YOU DO? _____

© 1996 by The Center for Applied Research in Education

Name _____

2–49 DOUBLE OH OH SEVEN

Each of these four-letter words have a double <u>o</u> in the middle. See if you can figure out all seven words from the definitions.

1. ___ O O ___ (what you get from a sheep's coat)

2. ___ O O ___ (below your ankle)

3. ___ O O ___ (part of plant that grows under the ground)

4. ___ O O ___ (what you eat)

5. ___ O O ___ (twelve o'clock midday)

6. ___ O O ___ (a good thing to read)

7. ___ O O ___ (the opposite of bad)

Which word spells the same both forward and backward? Circle its number.

2–50 LOOK OVER THE FOUR-LEAF CLOVER

© 1996 by The Center for Applied Research in Education

Look over this four-leaf clover and see how many words you can form. Each word must have three or more letters and use the middle letter of the clover. The letters do not have to be touching each other. One word will use all the letters!

Give yourself one point for each word, plus five bonus points if you figure out a word using all the letters. Do not use any words ending in s.

_____   _____

_____   _____

_____   _____

_____   _____

_____   _____

_____   _____

Hint for 5-letter word: I'm hard as a rock. __ __ __ __ __

Word Points   =   _____

Bonus Points   =   _____

Total Points   =   _____

2–51 FLOWER POWER

See how many words you can form from the letters in this flower. Each word must be two or more letters and use the middle letter of the flower. The letters do not have to be touching each other. One word will use all the letters!

You cannot use any letter more than once. Proper nouns and contractions are outlawed. Each word counts a point, but you get five extra points if you figure out the 7-letter word!

_____   _____   _____

_____   _____   _____

_____   _____   _____

_____   _____   _____

_____   _____   _____

_____   _____   _____

_____   _____   _____

_____   _____   _____

_____   _____   _____

_____   _____   _____

_____   _____   _____

Clue to 7-letter word: This flower is _ _ _ _ _ _ _ in the ground.

2–52 STAR POWER

See how many words you can make from the letters in this star. Each word must be three or more letters and use the middle letter of the star. The letters do not have to be touching each other. One word will use all the letters!

You cannot use any letter more than once. Proper nouns, words ending in <u>s</u>, and contractions are outlawed. Each word counts a point, but you get five extra points if you get the 6-letter word!

_____   _____   _____

_____   _____   _____

_____   _____   _____

_____   _____   _____

_____   _____   _____

_____   _____   _____

_____   _____   _____

_____   _____   _____

_____   _____   _____

_____   _____   _____

_____   _____   _____

Clue to 6-letter word: I'm soft and pale. I'm __ __ __ __ __ __ .

2–53 WORD SCRAMBLE SECRET

Fill in the letters of the words that fit the definitions. Then find the secret word using the letters in the circles. Write the secret word in the banner at the bottom of the page.

1. I have yellow kernels.

2. My happy face has one.

3. You can use me when you eat.

4. You can make a rhythm if you beat on me.

5. I am a type of musical group.

Secret Word Clue: I am often found in the sky.

Secret Word:

2–54 MONTHS AND HOLIDAYS

Use the holiday clues to fill in the names of the months of the year in the blanks provided.

1. _ _ _ _ **M** _ _ _ _

2. **O** _ _ _ _ _ _ _

3. _ _ **N** _ _ _ _

4. _ _ _ **T** _ _ _ _ _

5. _ _ _ _ **H**

6. _ _ _ _ **S** _

7. _ **O** _ _ _ _ _ _

8. **F** _ _ _ _ _ _ _

9. _ _ _ **Y**

10. _ _ _ **E**

11. _ **A** _

12. _ _ **R** _ _

CLUES:

1. Christmas

2. Halloween;
    Columbus Day

3. New Year's Day;
    Martin Luther
    King's Birthday

4. Grandparent's
    Day; Labor Day

5. International
    Women's Day;
    St. Patrick's Day

6. Summer Vacation

7. Veteran's Day;
    Thanksgiving

8. President's Day;
    Valentine's Day

9. Independence Day

10. Father's Day;
    Flag Day

11. Mother's Day;
    Memorial Day

12. Passover (often);
    Easter (often);
    Good Friday (often)

Name _____

2–55 WORD ORIGINS OF MONTHS AND DAYS OF WEEK

The following words represent the word origins of the months and days of the week. Guess what word each represents and put the month or day on the blank beside each. Then list in sequential order under the proper categories. The first one is done for you.

Junius	June	Moon	_____
octo	_____	Sun	_____
Saturn	_____	Janus	_____
novem	_____	septem	_____
februa	_____	aprilis	_____
Fria	_____	Tiw	_____
Thor	_____	Mars	_____
Augustus Caesar	_____	decem	_____
Julius Caesar	_____	Maia	_____
Woden	_____		

HINT: Do the ones you are sure of first. Then get the rest by adept guesses.

Months of Year

1. _____   5._____   9. _____

2. _____   6._____   10. _____

3. _____   7._____   11. _____

4. _____   8._____   12. _____

Days of Week

1. _____   5._____

2. _____   6._____

3. _____   7._____

4. _____

2–56 SIGNS OF THE TIMES

Imagine you see the following signs, but some of the letters on each sign are faded with age. See if you can fill in the letters you can't see. Then use the circled letters to form a sentence. The letters will be used in order.

1. EMERGE __ __ ◯ EXIT

2. __ ◯ NOT ENTER

3. NO __ ◯ MPING

4. ◯ __ EP WATER

5. BUS ST ◯ __

6. NO SMOK __ __ ◯

7. __ __ ◯ ST AID

8. NO __ __ ◯ SPASSING

9. ◯ __ ULTS ONLY

10. ◯ __ IS SIDE UP

11. __ __ ◯ ARE OF DOG

12. KEE __ ◯ FF

13. LIVE WI ◯ __ __

14. DON'T WA __ ◯

Put the circled letters in order to form a sentence meant just for you!

◯◯◯ ◯◯ ◯◯◯◯◯ ◯◯◯◯ !

2–57 SPORTS MATCH

Use the SPORTS WORDS box to help you match words that are used in each of these sports.

SPORTS WORDS		
hoop	tuck	tee
steal	puck	jab
turf	punt	love

1. HOCKEY _____

2. BOXING _____

3. TENNIS _____

4. BASEBALL _____

5. FOOTBALL _____

6. DIVING _____

7. HORSE RACING _____

8. BASKETBALL _____

9. GOLF _____

153

2–58 ASK A SILLY QUESTION

What did one wall say to the other wall?

Write the words that match the definitions on the blanks below. Then circle the first and last letters of each word. Read downward and you should get the answer to the riddle.

1. white worm   __ __ __ __ __ __

2. a planet   __ __ __ __ __

3. "bald" bird   __ __ __ __ __ __

4. wonderful   __ __ __ __ __ __ __ __ __

5. stringed toy   __ __ - __ __

6. paddle   __ __ __

7. one-horned animal   __ __ __ __ __ __ __ __

8. Lincoln's nickname   __ __ __

9. instructor   __ __ __ __ __ __ __

So, what did one wall say to the other wall?

_____

_____

_____

2–59 FIND THE MISSING BABIES

Names of baby animals are hidden in the letter below. Find all ten missing babies and put them beside their correct mothers. The first one is done for you. Be careful! Some baby names may be in two separate words!

Dear Ms. Farrow:

I have several lamb puppets which I have brought from Cuba. Despite all the kidding and fawning, the info all of you gave Cal for displaying them was correct. In the kit ten cubby holes hold the dolls for easy viewing.

Sincerely,

Vixen Colter

MOTHERS

1. MARE
2. CAT
3. NANNY GOAT
4. COW
5. EWE
6. DOE
7. JENNY
8. FOX
9. SOW
10. LIONESS

BABIES

COLT

2–60 FOURS

Some things come in fours. See how many you can work out.

Directions:

1._____

2._____

3._____

4._____

Seasons:

1._____

2._____

3._____

4._____

Human Limbs:

1._____

2._____

3._____

4._____

Kinds of Sentences:

1._____

2._____

3._____

4._____

2–61 ANY MONTH FUN

Spell whatever month it is on the short blanks below. Be sure the month is spelled exactly right. Then take turns down your row, around your table, or whatever way your teacher tells you. When it is your turn, write (and say aloud to the class) a word beginning with the next letter. **Example**: If the month is May, the first student might write <u>marble</u>; the second student, <u>apple</u>; the third student, <u>yellow</u>. The fourth student would start again with a word beginning with <u>M</u>.

Use this sheet to write your words and to think ahead to what letter you might have next and a word that starts with that letter. Do not use any words twice. If a student cannot think of a word, he or she says, "Pass." The next student must use that letter.

_____   _____

_____   _____

_____   _____

_____   _____

_____   _____

_____   _____

_____   _____

_____   _____

2–62 MEMORY RECALL

Write your name on this paper. Then turn it over. Your teacher will read you a list (twice) of five words beginning with the same letter. Do not write anything down until the teacher is finished. Then turn the paper over, try to recall as many words as you can, and spell them on the blanks below. The words do not need to be in the order they are read.

The teacher may read you other lists beginning with other letters. Do the same with these lists, trying again to recall from memory as many words as you can and to spell them correctly.

List I

_____

_____

_____

_____

_____

List II

_____

_____

_____

_____

List III

_____

_____

_____

_____

_____

List IV

_____

_____

_____

_____

2–63 FOLD IT/PASS IT ON

Write your name on one paper only. Write a vowel in the LAST large space (a, e, i, o, or u). Fold your paper UP on the dotted line so your letter cannot be seen, and pass it on to the next person in your row or at your table. Each person then puts one letter (not a vowel) in the next large space, folds UP along the next dotted line, and passes it on. When you get your paper back, unfold it and make as many words as you can from these letters. Your teacher will explain how to score.

- -

- -

- -

- -

- -

- -

- -

- -

2–64 MUSICAL CHAIR HOMOGRAPHS

To the Teacher: Set up chairs in a double row, back to back, with one chair less than the number of players up front. If convenient, use a record player and recorded music. If not, have an object on which to tap or drum during the game.

Number of Players: Entire class, eight up front at a time

Materials Needed:
- COMMON HOMOGRAPHS LIST (or other questions you prepare)
- 7 chairs
- Record player/record or CD player/cassette, if desired

How to Play: Students walk along the chairs while the teacher plays music or drums on an object. When the sound stops, students quickly find chairs and sit down. One player will be without a chair. If COMMON HOMOGRAPHS LIST is used, the teacher would say the word and use it in a sentence. The student would *say* another word that is spelled the same (but that has a different meaning), and use it in a sentence. (**Example**: yard/yard.)

Upon answering correctly, the student exchanges his or her standing position to be seated in the chair of any other player he or she chooses. That new standing student is then asked a question. Upon answering correctly, this student exchanges places with any other player, and so on. Upon answering *incorrectly,* the player must exchange places with someone *watching* the game. Thus, the person who has missed getting a chair *and* missed the question is "retired" into the general classroom seats until such times as he or she is re-chosen to play. Another round of music or tapping begins and the game continues. No chairs are removed. No rough-housing is allowed.

Rationale: By not removing chairs, no individual becomes the ultimate winner or loser. When a student misses getting a chair, he or she has a chance to "redeem" himself or herself by answering the question correctly and thus can continue to play. Even if the player is "retired" to the spectator group, there is a chance he or she will be picked later by another student who is "retired." The whole class—players and spectators—learn by hearing the questions and answers, and each has a chance of being picked to play at any time.

Modifications: Depending on student ages, a student could ask the questions, instead of the teacher. Older students might take turns asking questions they make up themselves. Some teachers may prefer to stick to the original game rules, and remove a chair each round, "retiring" the student to his or her seat, and ending up with one winner. Removing chairs can be motivating and fun if not used too often, but has the disadvantages of fewer students in active participation and the creation of a somewhat rowdier, more competitive atmosphere.

This game can be adapted to any concepts you want to teach or review by using appropriate questions. Questions should be specific, with only one plausible answer, to avoid controversies. Spelling lists that can be studied in advance are excellent to use.

© 1996 by The Center for Applied Research in Education

COMMON HOMOGRAPHS LIST

arms (weapons); arms (part of body)
ball (sphere); ball (dance)
band (music makers); band (strap)
bass (low musical sound); bass (fish)*
bear (animal); bear (carry)
bluff (steep embankment); bluff (fool)
boil (bubble); boil (skin sore)
bow (bend); bow (part of ship); bow (weapon)*
box (container); box (hit); box (shrub)
brush (tool); brush (undergrowth)
can (container); can (able)
case (container); case (condition)
colon (part of body); colon (punctuation mark)
count (royalty); count (number)
date (fruit); date (on calendar); date (companion)
down (feathers); down (direction); down (grassland)
duck (bird); duck (avoid); duck (cloth)
fan (admirer); fan (cooling device)
fast (quick); fast (starve)
fine (good quality); fine (payment for wrongdoing)
firm (hard); firm (company)
fly (insect); fly (move through air); fly (flap of cloth covering pant zipper)
fresh (new); fresh (bold)
gum (chewing treat); gum (mouth part)
hold (grasp); hold (part of ship)
jam (preserved fruit); jam (squeeze); jam (impromptu music)
lap (part of body); lap (course); lap (drink)
lean (slant); lean (thin)
left (direction); left (went)
lie (untruth); lie (recline)
loaf (lounge); loaf (bread)
lumber (wood); lumber (walk slowly)
mole (skin spot); mole (animal)
page (call); page (of paper); page (youth)
pen (for writing); pen (enclosure)
pitcher (container); pitcher (in baseball)
pop (sound); pop (popular); pop (father); pop (soda)
pound (weight); pound (kennel); pound (hit)
prune (fruit); prune (cut)
pupil (part of eye); pupil (student)
racket (for tennis); racket (scheme); racket (noise)
ring (circle); ring (sound of bell)
row (in a line); row (with oars); row (fight)*
sock (hit); sock (stocking)
tap (hit lightly); tap (faucet)
swallow (bird); swallow (gulp)
well (good); well (for water)

*Note that these homographs are pronounced differently.

2–65 COLOR BEADS

To the Teacher: Have students color the beads as labelled. Run off four sheets of bead cards. Cut into cards of equal size. Laminate, if possible. You will need four cards of each bead color, a total of 32 cards.

Number of Players: 2, 3, or 4

Materials Needed:
- COLOR BEADS GAME BOARD
- 32 COLOR BEADS CARDS with various shapes
- 1 marker for each player

How to Play: Stack the cards. Each player draws one card in turn and moves marker to nearest unoccupied bead on the board that is the same as that shown on the card. Player then puts the card on the bottom of the pack.

If a player moves to an incorrect color and another player notices it, the offending player must return to the beginning star. If a player lands on an occupied bead, the player that was already there must go back to the first unoccupied bead that is the same color that the player was on.

The object of the game is to get to the end star first.

Rationale: The object of this game is to familiarize students with the colors red, green, yellow, purple, blue, black, orange, and white. It is expected that by seeing the written colors on the cards, spelling of the colors will be reinforced, as well as the relationship between the color word and the color itself.

Modifications: Students (or you) can easily make another COLOR BEADS GAME BOARD with other colors as desired.

COLOR BEADS GAME BOARD

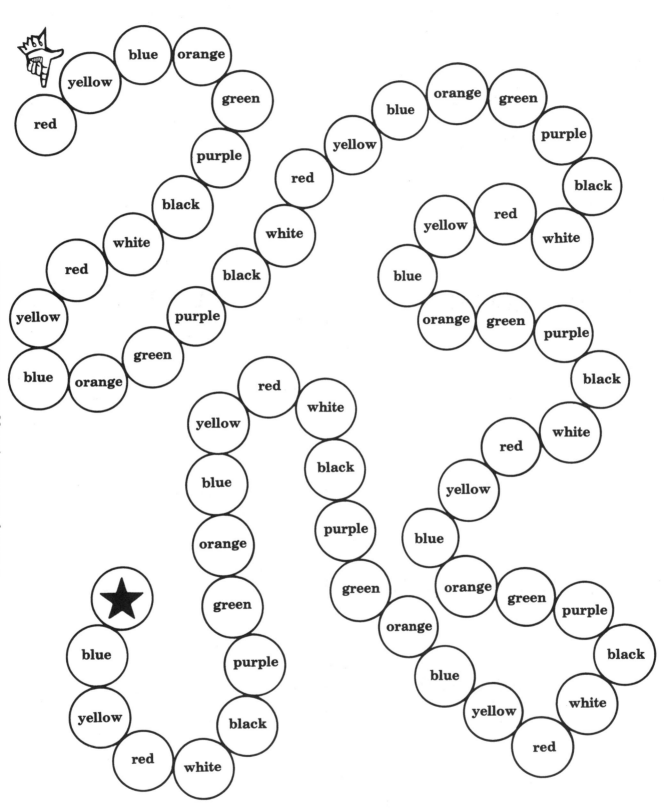

COLOR BEADS CARDS

RED	GREEN
YELLOW	PURPLE
BLUE	BLACK
ORANGE	WHITE

2–66 MOST COMMON WORDS CARDS

To the Teacher: The following three pages contain 48 of the 50 most common words in the English language. (Only <u>a</u> and <u>I</u> have been omitted.) These words make up more than one-third of all words used in printed material today! That is why it is so important that students recognize them on sight and be able to spell them correctly.

These words can be used in a variety of ways, from flash cards to game cards. To prepare for use:

1. Copy the pages on tagboard and laminate, if feasible. (or) Make the pages into plastic overhead transparencies.
2. Cut cards apart with paper cutter, being sure all cards are of uniform size.

If you want larger cards or different words, you could make cards using 3˝ × 5˝ or 4˝ × 6˝ index cards and a felt pen.

These other common words below add to the MOST COMMON WORDS CARDS to make up about half of all words in print!

about	long	see
been	look	so
call	made	some
come	make	than
could	many	them
day	may	then
did	more	these
down	my	time
find	no	two
first	now	up
get	number	water
go	oil	way
has	other	who
her	out	will
him	over	would
into	part	write
like	people	

A few examples of games in which these cards can be used:

AROUND THE WORLD (2–67)
SPELL MY WORD (2–68)
SPELL AND CHALLENGE (2–69)

MOST COMMON WORDS CARDS

the	it
of	he
and	was
to	for
in	on
is	are
you	as
that	with

MOST COMMON WORDS CARDS
(CONTINUED)

his	one
they	had
at	by
be	word
this	but
have	not
from	what
or	all

MOST COMMON WORDS CARDS
(CONTINUED)

were	an
we	each
when	which
your	she
can	do
said	how
there	their
use	if

2–67 AROUND THE WORLD

To the Teacher: For some reason, first and second graders love these two very simple games!

Number of Players: Entire class

Materials Needed: • MOST COMMON WORDS CARDS (48)

How to Play: Teacher holds up one card with word on it and shows it to the first two children in the row or at the table. First child to say the word correctly physically "travels" (exchanges places) down the row or around the table. The winner and the next person in the row vie for the next word.

Rationale: Practice makes perfect. Practice is more fun in a game than in a drill or exercise.

Modifications: Use any vocabulary, spelling, or other flash or game cards you wish. Game can be played with teams, keeping points instead of traveling. One class can challenge another class on words they both are studying. See N-18 for hints on choosing teams.

2–68 SPELL MY WORD

Number of Players: Entire class

Materials Needed:
• 1 blown-up balloon
• MOST COMMON WORDS CARDS

How to Play: Pass out one word to each member of the class. Bop a balloon to the class. The one who catches it begins the game. The beginning player says, "Spell my word," and then says his or her word with emphasis while bopping a balloon to another class member. That player catching the balloon must spell the word correctly.

If the player misspells the word, the original player repeats the routine and bops the balloon to another player. If the same player catches it, that player gets a second chance to spell the word. When a player spells the word correctly, that player says, "Spell my word," gives his or her word emphatically while bopping the balloon to still another player, and the game continues. No players are allowed to get out of their chairs to bop or receive balloons, but can stretch or reach.

Rationale: Balloon-bopping adds more fun and since it is hard to control where it goes, all players have an equal chance. (If players *choose* a person, sometimes the more popular get chosen more frequently, and those who need practice don't get it.) The balloon keeps attention, and everyone has to think about how to spell the word, because they don't know who will get the balloon!

Modification: Use any other spelling or word list.

2–69 SPELL AND CHALLENGE

To the Teacher:　　Run off cards, cut apart, and laminate, if feasible. Stack the cards in a pile face down near the front of the room.

Number of Players:　Entire class

Materials Needed:　• MOST COMMON WORDS CARDS

How to Play:　　Student comes to the front of the room and draws a card from the MOST COMMON WORDS CARDS pile, replacing it quickly on the bottom of the deck. Student uses the word in a sentence in front of the class—then spells the word. He or she can choose to spell it correctly or incorrectly. Anyone in the class can raise their hand and challenge the spelling.

If the word has been *incorrectly* spelled and is challenged, the challenger must spell it correctly. If the player does so, he or she then gets to go to the front and pick a card, and the game continues as before.

If the word has been incorrectly spelled and is challenged, and the challenger *also* misspells it, the player calls on someone else whose hand is raised. There is no penalty.

If the word was *correctly* spelled by the original player, and it is challenged (and therefore the challenger spells it incorrectly), there is no penalty. However, the original player gets an additional turn to draw another card.

If there are no challenges and the word is spelled correctly, the next student in the row or around the table draws a card, and the game continues.

Rationale:　　Having the student put the card away and think of how to use the word in a sentence diverts the student's attention for a moment. This makes the student remember how to spell it, rather than just immediately recalling the spelling. Challenges keep the game lively and interesting.

Modifications:　　This game can be played with any spelling or vocabulary words, or modified to practice other concepts.

Section Three

Language Arts, Mathematics, Social Studies, and Science

3–1 VALENTINE

Each heart contains the answer to one of the questions below.

I am a Valentine.

1. How many letters do I have?   1. _____

   Name: _____

2. How many syllables do I have?   2. _____

   Show: _____

3. How many vowels do I have?   3. _____

   Name: _____

4. How many consonants do I have?   4. _____

   Name: _____

5. How many repeated letters do I have?   5. _____

   Name: _____

6. How many capital letters do I have?   6. _____

   Name: _____

7. How many small letters do I have?   7. _____

   Name: _____

8. How many <u>different</u> letters do I have?   8. _____

   Name: _____

9. How many two-, three-, or four-letter words are inside me
   (with the letters in order)?   9. _____

   List: _____

   _____

3–2 SENTENCES TO DIVIDE AND CONQUER

Figure out the words that form the sentences below and write the sentence on the lines provided. They are divided improperly, but are in the correct order. If you divide them correctly, you will conquer the truth.

Example:　C anyo ufig ureo utt hisen ten ce?
Answer:　　Can you figure out this sentence?

1. Wed ne sda yisad ayo fthew eek.

_____

2. Fe bru aryist hese condmo ntho fthey ear.

_____

3. Fal landa utu mna reth esam esea son.

_____

4. Sum meri shot.

_____

5. Re dan dblu ear eco lors.

_____

3–3 SENTENCE SENSE

To be a sentence, a group of words must have a subject and a verb. It also has to make sense! Remember, a sentence can make a statement, ask a question, make a request, or express an emotion.

Sort out the following groups of words. If they make a sentence, put the correct punctuation at the end of the group of words. Also circle the letter in front of each complete sentence, and write the letter on the line below. Then unscramble these letters to form a secret word.

A   1. The moon is silver

B   2. My father and mother

C   3. Happy, sad, and more

D   4. In the middle of the night

E   5. They were very happy

F   6. The stars and stripes

G   7. What a day that was

R   8. Put it there

S   9. The fuzzy, little cat

T   10. Who is he

U   11. Members of the team

V   12. Salt and pepper

W   13. A day that never

X   14. In the very beginning

CIRCLED LETTERS: _____

SECRET WORD UNSCRAMBLED: _____

3–4 MERCEDES, THE CAT

Run-on sentences are those that run together, usually with no punctuation. Instead of stopping at the end of a complete thought, they just keep on going, like the Everready Bunny on TV! Sometimes run-on sentences are strung together with commas, but this is not correct, either.

Find the LAST WORD of each sentence. Write them on the lines provided.

1. _____   5. _____

2. _____   6. _____

3. _____   7. _____

4. _____   8. _____

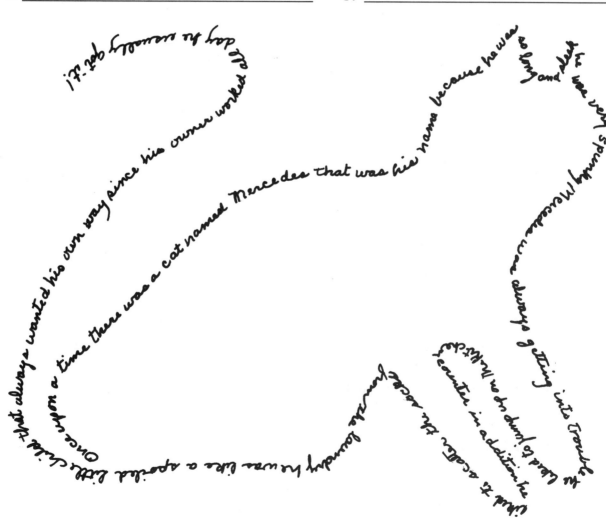

© 1996 by The Center for Applied Research in Education

3–5 PUNCTUATION RIDDLES

1. You raise your voice when you see me.
   I expect an answer.
   I look like a cup hook.
   Who am I?

   _____

2. You usually stop when you see me.
   I end it all.
   My nickname is "Dot."
   Who am I?

   _____

3. You pause when you see me.
   I am very popular.
   I look like a half-circle.
   Who am I?

   _____

4. You show excitement when you see me.
   I am tall and thin.
   I have two parts.
   Who am I?

   _____

5. You know I'm talking when you see me.
   My partner and I are a pair.
   Half of me looks like a double comma.
   Who am I?

   _____

3–6 CONTRACTIONS DETECTIVE

Be a detective and find the letter or letters that have been left out to form the contractions (shortened forms) below. Then write out the two words that each contraction stands for.

Example: didn't = did not (the <u>o</u> has been left out to form the contraction).

CONTRACTIONS	MISSING LETTERS	FULL WORDS	
1. doesn't	_____	_____	_____
2. don't	_____	_____	_____
3. hadn't	_____	_____	_____
4. he's	_____	_____	_____
5. here's	_____	_____	_____
6. I'm	_____	_____	_____
7. isn't	_____	_____	_____
8. she's	_____	_____	_____
9. that's	_____	_____	_____
10. there's	_____	_____	_____
11. what's	_____	_____	_____
12. who's	_____	_____	_____

© 1996 by The Center for Applied Research in Education

hasn't = has not

HINT: The apostrophes (') indicate where letters are missing.

3–7 CHANGING NOUNS WITH T

Put a <u>t</u> in front of the correct word from the WORD BANK to form a new word for each clue.

1. _ _ _ _ _ _   locomotive

2. _ _ _ _   musical sound

3. _ _ _ _   adhesive

4. _ _ _ _   a rip

5. _ _ _ _   story

6. _ _ _ _   look alike

7. _ _ _ _   rubber wheel

8. _ _ _   money government collects

9. _ _ _ _ _   path

10. _ _ _ _ _   garbage

WORD BANK			
ape	ale	ax	ear
ire	one		rail
rain	rash		win

3–8 NOUN–VERB WORDS

Each word in the NOUN–VERB WORD BANK can be used as either a noun or verb. **Example**: <u>Can</u> you buy a <u>can</u> of beans? Show you know the difference by choosing at least five words and using them in a paragraph or story. <u>Use each chosen word as both a noun and verb!</u> In your paragraph circle all words you chose from the word bank.

_____

_____

_____

_____

_____

_____

_____

_____

_____

_____

_____

_____

NOUN–VERB WORD BANK

Choose 5

act	can	fool	picture
bank	change	hide	race
bear	check	hurt	rain
bill	crow	jam	run
block	date	jump	sail
box	duck	list	show
brand	fall	mail	stick
buck	fly	part	wreck

3–9 PLURAL TIC-TAC-TOE

Play tic-tac-toe with a partner. Your goal is to win the game with a straight line (up and down, across, or diagonal) that includes ONLY PLURAL NOUNS.

DOG	BUS	DEER
LAKES	MEN	CHILD
PIGS	GRASS	GIRLS

How to Play PLURAL TIC-TAC-TOE:

1. Two people play, and take turns marking squares on one sheet.

2. Each player tries to pick a square with a plural word in it.

3. Alternating turns, each player marks a square with a giant "X."

4. Each player tries to get three PLURAL words forming a straight line in any direction.

5. The player who first gets the correct tic-tac-toe (straight line) wins.

Hints:
- Plural means more than one.
- There is only one correct tic-tac-toe solution.

3–10 CONTRACTION RELAY

Each team uses one sheet of paper like this. Your first team member writes a contraction in the first space provided and passes it on. The second team member writes a different contraction in the second space and passes it on. This continues until everyone on your team has participated. You can start again with team member 1 and go through your team members as long as they can think of new contractions, but no member can write out of turn or more than one contraction at a time. If you cannot think of a contraction, pass the paper quickly to the next team member. The last one on your team rushes to the chalkboard and copies the contractions from your team's paper and takes a seat. The team with the most CORRECT contractions wins. If there is a tie in number of contractions, the first chalkboard-writer to be seated is the team that wins.

1.   18.
2.   19.
3.   20.
4.   21.
5.   22.
6.   23.
7.   24.
8.   25.
9.   26.
10.   27.
11.   28.
12.   29.
13.   30.
14.   31.
15.   32.
16.   33.
17.   34.

3–11 ACTING OUT ACTION VERBS (GRADE 1)

Teacher: Run off this page of action verbs on a copy machine. Cut into cards. Place in a stack face-down. Have student draw one card from stack, show it to you, and pantomime action word for the class. Student calls on another student to guess. If correct, that student draws card and pantomimes. If wrong, student calls on another student until guessed correctly. This fun game helps with sight reading, spelling, and recognition of action verbs.

bake	push
bite	rake
cut	ride
dig	run
feed	set
hide	sit
hop	slam
hug	sock
mop	step
pick	tug

3–12 ACTING OUT ACTION VERBS (GRADE 2)

Teacher: Run off this page of action verbs on a copy machine. Cut into cards. Place in a stack face-down. Have student draw one card from stack, show it to you, and pantomime action word for the class. Student calls on another student to guess. If correct, that student draws card and pantomimes. If wrong, student calls on another student until guessed correctly. This fun game helps with sight reading, spelling, and recognition of action verbs.

bat	hit
chop	jump
clap	kick
cry	kiss
dress	plant
drink	play
drive	read
fall	rub
fan	wash
fly	wink

3–13 ACTING OUT ACTION VERBS (GRADE 3)

Teacher: Run off this page of action verbs on a copy machine. Cut into cards. Place in a stack face-down. Have student draw one card from stack, show it to you, and pantomime action word for the class. Student calls on another student to guess. If correct, that student draws card and pantomimes. If wrong, student calls on another student until guessed correctly. This fun game helps with sight reading, spelling, and recognition of action verbs.

blow	scrub
chew	shake
close	shoot
cover	skate
crawl	slide
dance	smile
drop	splash
fight	swim
paint	throw
scratch	write

3–14 A-TISKET-A-TASKET ACTION VERBS

To the Teacher: This old game still holds the interest of younger pupils. The game can be played without the ALPHABET CARDS and basket with modification shown below.

Number of Players: Entire class or smaller group

Materials Needed:
- ALPHABET CARDS
- Basket or box

How to Play: Players sit in a circle or in their seats. First player draws a letter from the box, not showing it to anyone else except the teacher. This player walks or skips around behind seated players while all players chant, "A-tisket, a-tasket, a green and yellow basket; I sent a letter to my love and on the way I dropped it. I dropped it . . . I dropped it . . ."

First player drops the alphabet letter behind any player, saying an action verb beginning with that letter. The second player gets up and tries to catch the first player, but both players are required to use the action said by the first player. (**Examples:** run, skip, jump, waddle.) All the while the first player tries to get into the second player's seated position. If the first player succeeds in sitting in the second player's spot, the game continues with the second player becoming "it." The second player then draws a letter from the box, the chant begins, and the game proceeds. If, however, the first player gets caught before he or she gets seated in the second player's spot, that player must give another action verb beginning with the letter he or she dropped. He or she must also be "it" for another turn.

Rationale: Kids love this because of the physical action, and learn about action verbs without realizing it! They also enjoy thinking ahead, so when their turns come, they are ready with clumsy and entertaining actions.

Modification: For a simpler, faster-moving game, don't use alphabet letters. Just have players say any appropriate action verbs.

3–15 I-HAVE-A-BOOK ADJECTIVES

To the Teacher: To make this game simpler for younger pupils, stick to one letter and one item, repeatedly asking the same question, instead of changing letters. For older students, you could make the requirements harder, such as requiring alliteration (*cautious child*).

Number of Players: Entire class

How to Play: Leader (teacher or student) chooses a common letter of the alphabet and says, "My letter is _____. I have a book. What kind of book?" Leader then calls on a student. The called-upon student answers with an adjective (serious or humorous) beginning with the designated letter. Called-upon student then becomes "leader" and continues in same way.

Example:

(LEADER)	My letter is <u>r</u>. I have a book. What kind of book?
(STUDENT 1)	A <u>red</u> book.
(STUDENT 1)	My letter is <u>b</u>. I have a face. What kind of face?
(STUDENT 2)	A <u>blank</u> face.
(STUDENT 2)	My letter is <u>f</u>. I have a banana. What kind of banana?
(STUDENT 3)	A <u>flaky</u> banana.

No adjective can be repeated. If a player makes a mistake, the teacher should point it out and get the game back on track. If a student gives the wrong first letter for the adjective, the player presenting the letter and question must call on another student.

Rationale: Students get practice with letters of the alphabet, sounds of the letters, and get a *feel* for adjectives as describing words.

Modifications: You can practice nouns, adverbs, prepositional phrases and other parts of speech by modifying the questions.

Example (nouns):

(LEADER)	My letter is <u>c</u>. Who am I?
(STUDENT 1)	I am a <u>cat</u>.
(STUDENT 1)	My letter is <u>m</u>. Who am I?
(STUDENT 2)	I am a <u>monster</u>.

Example (adverbs):

(LEADER)	My letter is <u>c</u>. How do I run?
(STUDENT 1)	I run <u>carefully</u>.

Example (prepositional phrases):

(LEADER)	My letter is <u>s</u>. Where am I going?
(STUDENT 1)	I am going to the <u>store</u>.
(STUDENT 1)	My letter is <u>c</u>. Where am I going?
(STUDENT 2)	I am going in <u>circles</u>.

3–16 <u>M</u> IS FOR MATH

These words are used often in math. They all begin with <u>m</u>. Use the clues to figure them out and write the rest of the word in the blank.

1. **M** _____ (subtract)

2. **M** _____ (almost all of)

3. **M** _____ (newest measuring system)

4. **M** _____ (a small amount of time)

5. **M** _____ (put two alike things together)

6. **M** _____ (like a yard, but a little more)

7. **M** _____ (like add, only faster)

8. **M** _____ (to determine length, etc.)

9. **M** _____ (the center)

10. **M** _____ (average)

How many climbers?

_____

Name _____

3–17 EASY MATH PROGRESSIONS

Figure out the number that would logically be the next in the progression. **HINT**: You may want to add, subtract, multiply, or divide to figure out the relationships.

1.	1	2	3	_____	5	6	7
2.	12	10	8	_____	4	2	0
3.	2	4	8	_____	32	64	128
4.	28	24	20	_____	12	8	4
5.	5	10	15	_____	25	30	35
6.	3	6	9	_____	15	18	21
7.	100	200	300	_____	500	600	700
8.	1	5	2	_____	3	7	4
9.	20	17	19	_____	18	15	17

Give each of your answers the code letter below. Then unscramble the letters to find out how well you did.

4	=	X
6	=	L
12	=	N
16	=	E
20	=	C
400	=	T

Dive right in!

___ ___ ___ ___ ___ ___ ___ ___ ___ !

3–18 SHORTCUTS

Sometimes when taking notes, people take a shortcut by making up their own abbreviations. For example, to say there are four quarts in a gallon, they might jot down:

4 q in a g

See how many of these shortcuts you can figure out.

1. 2 c in a p _____

2. 2 p in a q _____

3. 4 q in a g _____

4. 8 o in a c _____

5. 16 t in a c _____

6. 12 m in a y _____

7. 7 d in a w _____

8. 52 w in a y _____

9. 365 d in a y _____

10. 60 s in a m _____

11. 60 m in an h _____

12. 24 h in a d _____

13. 12 i in a f _____

14. 3 f in a y _____

15. 26 l in the a _____

© 1996 by The Center for Applied Research in Education

3–19 WHAT'S NEXT?

These items are in an order that makes sense. Can you figure out what comes next? Put your answers on the lines.

1.   _____

2.    _____

3.   _____

4.   _____

5. $A\,a \quad C\,c \quad E\,e$ _____

5.   _____

3–20 SPELLING WITH ROMAN NUMERALS

Below is a list of some of the Roman numerals and their more familiar equivalents. Using these clues, see if you can make words by Roman numeral "letters" for the numerals in parentheses below. The first one is done for you.

I = 1
II = 2
III = 3
IV = 4
V = 5
VI = 6
VII = 7
VIII = 8

IX = 9
X = 10
XI = 11
L = 50
C = 100
D = 500
M = 1000

1. F (4) E   FIVE _____

2. (100) 0 (50) (500)   _____

3. (50) (1) (500)   _____

4. (1000) (9)   _____

5. (500) (1) (1000)   _____

6. S (9)   _____

7. (100) 0 (500)   _____

3–21 FROZEN YOGURT PIE GRAPH

A pie graph is a circle picture of information. Put the information given into a pie graph and answer the questions. **Hint**: Be sure to label each area by flavor. Use the marks on the edge of the circle to help you.

INFORMATION TO GRAPH: There were 10 children. They all liked nonfat frozen yogurt, but not the same kind. Five children liked peach best; three children liked berry best; and the rest liked vanilla best.

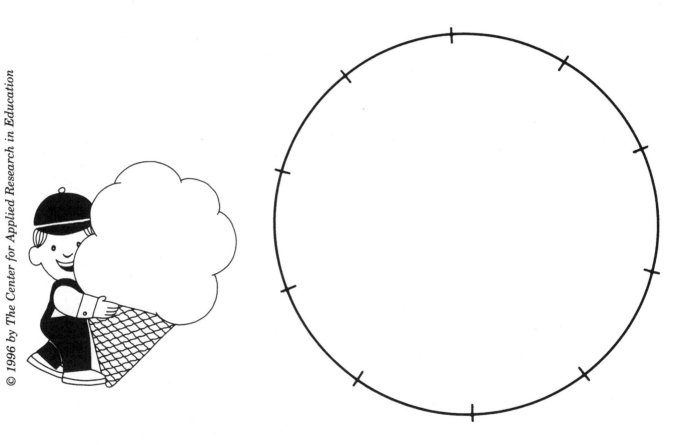

1. What was the flavor most children liked best? _____

2. How many children like vanilla best?_____

3. What flavor do **YOU** like best? _____

3–22 HOLIDAY DATES

Use the codes given and the HOLIDAY NUMBERS GRID to find the date for each of these holidays. WRITE OUT the months under the month column and put the day under the day column.

HOLIDAY (MONTH/DAY)	MONTH	DAY
1. **Yom Kippur (D1/D2)** (*varies*)	_____	_____
2. **Mother's Day (C1/A1)** (*varies*)	_____	_____
3. **Father's Day (B3/D4)** (*varies*)	_____	_____
4. **St. Patrick's Day (B4/A4)**	_____	_____
5. **Columbus Day (D1/D3)** (*varies*)	_____	_____
6. **Valentine's Day (B2/A1)**	_____	_____
7. **Groundhog Day (B2/B2)**	_____	_____
8. **Memorial Day (C1/A3)** (*varies*)	_____	_____
9. **Pearl Harbor Day (B1/A2)**	_____	_____
10. **Veteran's Day (C3/C3)**	_____	_____
11. **Independence Day (A2/D2)**	_____	_____
12. **Martin Luther King, Jr. Day (C2/C4)**	_____	_____
13. **New Year's Day (C2/C2)**	_____	_____

1	= JANUARY
2	= FEBRUARY
3	= MARCH
4	= APRIL
5	= MAY
6	= JUNE
7	= JULY
8	= AUGUST
9	= SEPTEMBER
10	= OCTOBER
11	= NOVEMBER
12	= DECEMBER

Holiday Numbers Grid

	1	2	3	4
D	10	4	9	18
C	5	1	11	16
B	12	2	6	3
A	14	7	30	17

3–23 FEBRUARY FUN

Write the day in February that these events happen. Then figure out the five answers below. You may use a calendar, dictionary, or encyclopedia to help you if you do not know the days. The NUMBER BANK has all the numbers you will need.

A. Lincoln's Birthday: _____

B. Washington's Birthday: _____

C. Valentine's Day: _____

D. Groundhog Day: _____

1. B   –   A   =   _____

2. B   –   C   =   _____

3. A   +   D   =   _____

4. C   +   D   =   _____

5. A   +   B   +   C   +   D   =   _____

```
NUMBER BANK

2   8   10   12   14
   14   16   22   50
```

3–24 EASY MATH SQUARES

Put numbers in the blank squares so the answers reading across and down are true.

1.

1	+		=	4
+		−		+
	−		=	
=		=		=
5		1		6

2.

2	x		=	10
x		x		÷
	÷		=	
=		=		=
12		15		5

3–25 MATH SPELLING

Add and subtract the number words and put the answers in the squares.

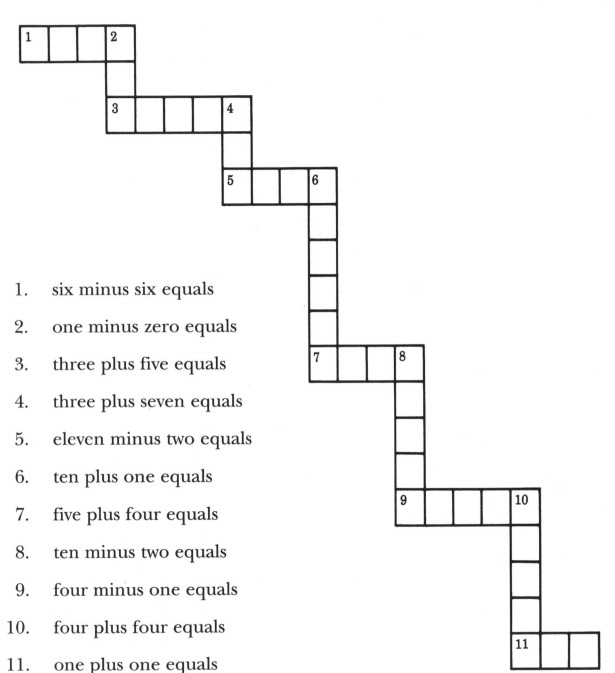

1. six minus six equals

2. one minus zero equals

3. three plus five equals

4. three plus seven equals

5. eleven minus two equals

6. ten plus one equals

7. five plus four equals

8. ten minus two equals

9. four minus one equals

10. four plus four equals

11. one plus one equals

3–26 IT ALL ADDS UP

Put the number that best fits in each blank. Then follow the plus signs and see if it all adds up.

1. _____ nose

   +

2. _____ to a pair

   +

3. _____ sides to a triangle

   +

4. _____ lucky clover leaves

   =

   _____

5. _____ feet to a yard

   +

6. _____ eyes

   +

7. _____ sides to a square

   +

8. _____ mouth

   =

   _____

If the total for numbers 1 through 4 equals the total for numbers 5 through 8, you are in the top 10!

Name _____

3–27 ODDS AND EVENS

Pretend you are a busy bee and buzz through this honeycomb. Begin where it says <u>Start</u> and top where it says <u>Finish</u>. You must move through the beehive one cell at a time and always to a new touching cell. As you buzz along, the cell where you are and the one you go to must add up to an even number.

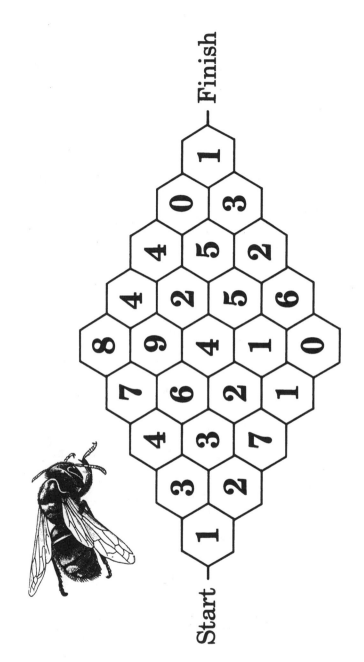

Name _____

3–28 A FEW BIG STATES

Put the states in the STATE BANK on the ladder in alphabetical order. The biggest state is already in the star.

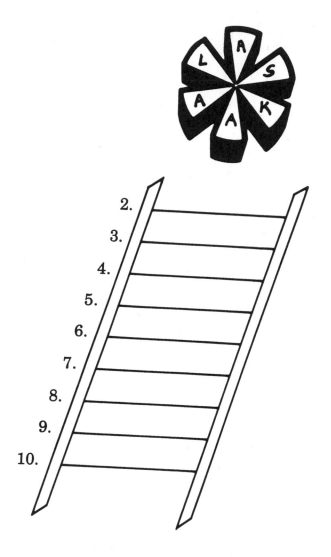

1. ALASKA

2.

3.

4.

5.

6.

7.

8.

9.

10.

STATE BANK		
Texas	Arizona	Utah
California	Oregon	Idaho
Montana	Nevada	Wyoming

© 1996 by The Center for Applied Research in Education

3–29 CAREER SEARCH

Go from left to right and figure out where to stop. Find eight careers and list them below.

T	E	A	C	H	E	R	P	L	U	M
B	E	R	E	L	E	C	T	R	I	C
I	A	N	N	U	R	S	E	S	E	C
R	E	T	A	R	Y	P	O	S	T	M
A	N	P	I	L	O	T	C	O	O	K

1. _____

2. _____

3. _____

4. _____

5. _____

6. _____

7. _____

8. _____

3–30 PEOPLE CONNECTIONS

Make a connection between the following famous people and their claim to fame. Put the correct letter of the person in front of the occupation.

_____ 1. President   a. John Glenn

_____ 2. Musician   b. Steffi Graf

_____ 3. Author   c. Bill Clinton

_____ 4. Artist   d. Judy Blume

_____ 5. Athlete   e. Tim Allen

_____ 6. Scientist   f. Tom Hanks

_____ 7. Astronaut   g. Elton John

_____ 8. Newscaster   h. Georgia O'Keeffe

_____ 9. Movie Star   i. Albert Einstein

_____ 10. TV Star   j. Peter Jennings

Name _____

3–31 PRESIDENT'S DAY

You don't have to be an artist to get a president for this holiday. Just draw each code square in the matching square on the grid.

| 1B | 1C | 2B | 2C | 3B | 3C | 3D | 3E | 3F | 4B |

| 4C | 4D | 4F | 5B | 5C | 5D | 5E | 5F | 6B | 6C |

| 6F | 7B | 7C | 7E | 7F | 8B | 8C | 8F | 9B | 9C |

| 9E | 9F | 10B | 10C | 10D | 10E | 10F | 11B | 11C | 11D |

	A	B	C	D	E	F	G
1							
2							
3							
4							
5							
6							
7							
8							
9							
10							
11							

Name the president you have drawn. _____

3–32 WHERE WOULD YOU BE?

You are given three clues for each puzzle. Write the COUNTRY where you would be on the blanks below. The circled letters form a special message to tell you how well you did.

1. Where would you be if:
   a. you rode in a double-decker bus?
   b. you saw the Tower of London?
   c. you watched the Changing of the Guard at Buckingham Palace?

2. Where would you be if:
   a. you ate frankfurters?
   b. you saw the city of Hamburg?
   c. you floated down the Rhine River?

3. Where would you be if:
   a. you visited the World Trade Center?
   b. you skated at Rockefeller Center?
   c. you saw several Broadway shows?

4. Where would you be if:
   a. you made change in yen?
   b. you saw thousands of cars being made for shipment to U.S.?
   c. you saw the city of Tokyo?

5. Where would you be if:
   a. you travelled by gondola down the canals?
   b. you toured Columbus's birthplace?
   c. you saw the city of Rome?

(1.) __ __ ◯ __ __ __ __

(2.) __ __ ◯ __ __ __ __

(3.) __ __ __ __ ◯ __ __ __ __ __ __ __ __

(4.) __ ◯ __ __ __

(5.) __ ◯ __ __ __

Name _____

3–33 SAY WHAT?

Turn the two wheels in your mind until the proper sounds match the animals. List them below.

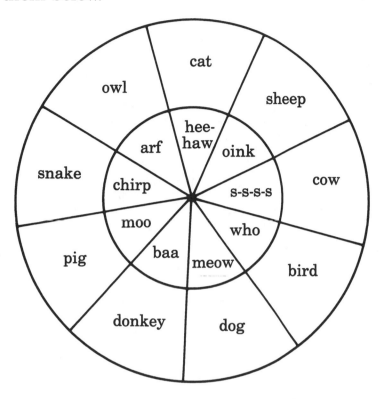

Animals

_____

_____

_____

_____

_____

_____

_____

Sounds

_____

_____

_____

_____

_____

_____

_____

3–34 JUST CALL ME A GROUP!

Turn the two wheels in your mind until the proper group terms match the animals. List them below.

Animals

_____

_____

_____

_____

_____

_____

_____

_____

_____

Group Name

_____

_____

_____

_____

_____

_____

_____

_____

_____

Name _____

3–35 BIG ONES/LITTLE ONES

Look at the names of the big ones in the vertical box. Write the names that their little ones would be called in the horizontal boxes. Use the LITTLE ONES word box to help you.

Example:

COW | calf

1. CAT

2. DOG

3. HORSE

4. PIGEON

5. KANGAROO

6. SWAN

LITTLE ONES: cygnet   whelp   kitten   squab   joey   foal

Name _____

3–36 HORSING AROUND

Begin in the center and find nine breeds of horses. List them in order on the lines provided.

B		O	S	A	C	L	Y	D	E	S
A		O								D
R		L		P	A	L	O	M		A
A		A		N				I		L
K		P		A		M		N		E
R		P		G	R	O		O		B
U		A						S		E
T		D	N	A	L	T	E	H		L
N										G
O	R	E	H	C	R	E	P	N	A	I

1. _____

2. _____

3. _____

4. _____

5. _____

6. _____

7. _____

8. _____

9. _____

3–37 ANIMAL APPETITES

Use the FOOD BANK to show you know how to satisfy these animal appetites.

1. | birds | eat > | |

2. | cows | eat > | |

3. | horses | eat > | |

4. | cats | .eat > | |

5. | mice | eat > | |

6. | bears | eat > | |

FOOD BANK
cheese   fish   grass   honey   hay   berries

3–38 HERE, KITTY, KITTY

Divide the cats on the fence into kinds of cats and put them in the correct boxes. **Hint**: Word length is your best clue.

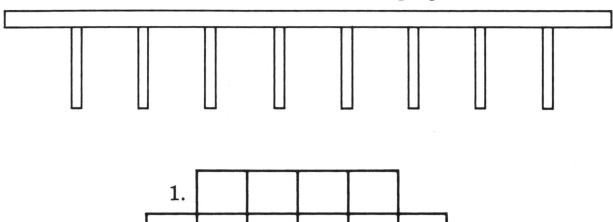

siamesemanxchinchillashorthairangorapersian

1.

2.

3.   S

4.

5.

6.

3–39 HOLIDAY PLANTS AND ANIMALS

Put the words in the outline. The names of holidays are major topics. Put related animals under <u>A</u>. Put related plants under <u>B</u>. Use the number of lines to guide you.

I. _ _ _ _ _ _ _ _ _

   A. _ _ _ _ _ _ _

   B. _ _ _ _ _ _ _ _ _

II. _ _ _ _ _ _

   A. _ _ _ _ _

   B. _ _ _ _

III. _ _ _ _ _ _ _ _ _

   A. _ _ _

   B. _ _ _ _ _ _

IV. _ _ _ _ _ _ _ _ _ _ _

   A. _ _ _ _ _ _

   B. _ _ _ _ _ _ _ _ _

HOLIDAY WORD BANK

poinsettia	turkey	Easter	cranberries
cat	Christmas	bunny	lily
Thanksgiving	pumpkin	reindeer	Halloween

3–40 TROPICAL OCEAN FISH

Circle any double letters in the following list of tropical ocean fish.
Example: <u>snapper</u> (The <u>p</u> is doubled.)

Write one of each doubled letter on the line. Then unscramble these letters to answer the question at the bottom of the page.

angelfish	grouper
barracuda	moray
bass	puffer
batfish	sailfish
devilfish	seahorse
goatfish	snook
goby	wahoo

Which letters are doubled? _____

What helps keep us dry in rainy weather? _____

3–41 DO YOU KNOW YOUR CRUSTACEANS?

Follow the four simple directions and you should end up with some common crustaceans. (Crustaceans are hard-shelled, spineless creatures with jointed legs and segmented bodies.)

sailfish	shrimp	batfish
lobster	seahorse	barnacle
angelfish	crab	goatfish
devilfish	prawn	goby
ostracod	snapper	grouper

1. Cross out words beginning with g.
2. Cross out words with "fish" in them.
3. Cross out words beginning with s.
4. List the words that are left:

_____   _____

_____   _____

_____   _____

The list above are the shelled creatures. The ones you crossed out are all tropical ocean fish.

3–42
WHAT DO THESE WORDS HAVE IN COMMON?

Many of these words may be unfamiliar, but they all have something in common. See if you can unscramble the circled code letters to find out what it is.

S N A I L

C O Q U I N A

M U S S E (L)

T R I T O N

N A U T I (L) U S

L I M P E T

C L A M

O Y (S) T E R

C O N C H

(S) C A L L O P

M U R E X

C O C K L E

W H (E) L K

V O L U T E

A B A L O N E

Q U A (H) O G

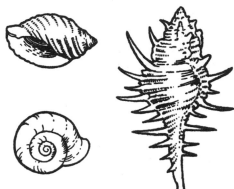

Put your circled code letters here. _____

Unscramble the code letters. What do these items have in common?

_____

3–43 REPTILES

These cold-blooded vertebrates have more in common than bony skeletons, lungs, and scaly or plated bodies. Their names all hide common three-letter words. Write the words in the boxes beside the name of the reptile. Give yourself extra credit if you find extra words!

1. alligator
2. crocodile
3. chameleon
4. dragon
5. adder
6. cobra
7. rattlesnake
8. terrapin
9. garter
10. agama
11. gavial
12. chuckwalla
13. anaconda
14. copperhead
15. racer
16. tuatara

Bonus Words:

215

3–44 BUGABOO

These bug balloons are all tangled up! Untangle them and put the circled letters in the boxes. What you find may be just what you need.

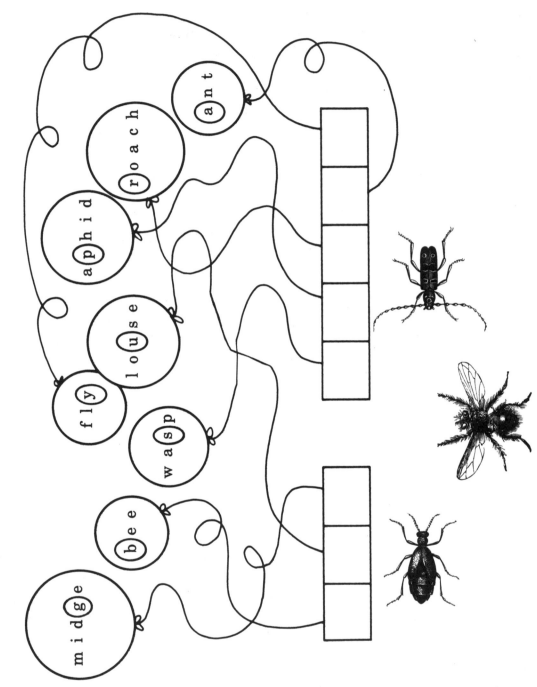

3–45 A BUSY WOODPECKER

A busy woodpecker seems to have pecked all the vowels from these trees. You can see how important vowels are! All the trees shown here have their consonants in order. Figure out the missing vowels, and write the correct type of wood in the boxes.

1. cdr

2. fr

3. hmlck

4. rdwd

5. pn

6. sprc

7. sh

8. spn

9. bsswd

10. bch

11. brch

12. chrry

13. lm

14. gm

15. hckry

16. mpl

17. k

18. tlp

19. wlnt

20. wllw

3-46 MISSED YOU

Fill in the missing letter in each planet below.

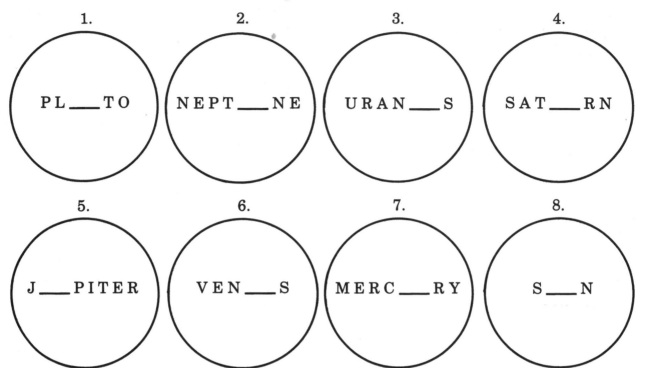

1. PL __ TO
2. NEPT __ NE
3. URAN __ S
4. SAT __ RN
5. J __ PITER
6. VEN __ S
7. MERC __ RY
8. S __ N

Can you name two other planets?

9. _____
   (where you live)

10. _____
    (a candy bar name)

Name _____

3–47 WATER BIRDS

These water birds seem to have swallowed some three-letter words. See how many of them you can find. Some of the birds weren't hungry, though!

albatross	gannet	murre
auk	goose	pelican
booby	grebe	penguin
cormorant	gull	plover
coot	heron	puffin
curlew	kittiwake	stork
bittern	loon	swan
crane	mallard	tern

1. _____

2. _____

3. _____

4. _____

5. _____

6. _____

7. _____

8. _____

9. _____

10. _____

11. _____

12. _____

13. _____

14. _____

15. _____

16. _____

List the birds that did not eat any three-letter words:

17. _____

18. _____

19. _____

20. _____

21. _____

22. _____

23. _____

24. _____

3–48 EASY ADD-A-LETTER FOODS

Add a letter from the LETTER BANK to each of the words below to form a new word. Each new word will be something good to eat.

LETTERS	PLUS	WORDS	EQUAL	FOODS
1. _____	+	ear	=	_____
2. _____	+	range	=	_____
3. _____	+	ilk	=	_____
4. _____	+	eat	=	_____
5. _____	+	each	=	_____
6. _____	+	live	=	_____
7. _____	+	am	=	_____

LETTER BANK

h   m   m   o   o   p   p

© 1996 by The Center for Applied Research in Education

Appendix One
GENERIC AIDS

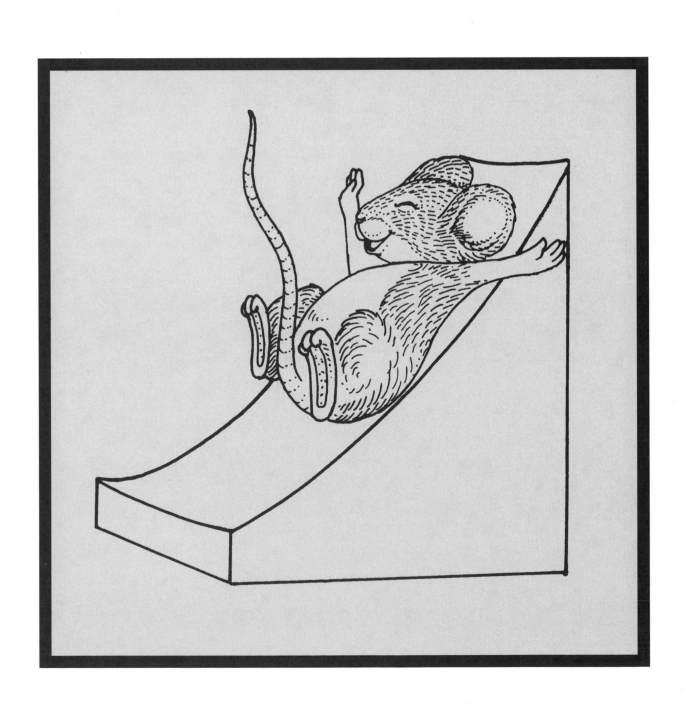

GAME CARDS

The following four pages contain cards for use in large and small groups. The sheets can be used in a variety of ways, from flash cards to game cards to response cards to teacher questions or examples. ALPHABET CARDS, PHONOGRAM CARDS, and others are located elsewhere near explanations of specific games. The list below details the cards contained in this section.

1. **Punctuation**
   a. Period
   b. Question mark
   c. Exclamation point
   d. Quotation marks
2. **Types of Sentences**
   a. Declarative (Statement)
   b. Interrogative (Question)
   c. Exclamatory (Strong Feeling)
   d. Imperative (Request)
3. **Parts of Speech**
   a. Helping verb
   b. Linking verb
   c. Noun
   d. Adjective
4. **Miscellaneous**
   a. Yes/No
   b. Same/Different
   c. A/B/C/D
   d. 1/2/3/4
   e. Small Alphabet Letters

To prepare for use:

1. Copy the pages on tagboard and laminate, if feasible; or make the pages with plastic overhead transparencies.
2. Cut cards apart with paper cutter, being sure all cards are of uniform size.

GAME CARDS

●	?
!	" "
Declarative (statement)	**Interrogative (question)**
Exclamatory (strong feeling)	**Imperative (request)**

Helping Verb	**Linking Verb**
Noun	**Adjective**
YES	**NO**
SAME	**DIFFERENT**

A	**B**
C	**D**
1	**2**
3	**4**

SMALL ALPHABET LETTERS

(number of each according to how common)

A	A	A	A	A	A	A	A	A
E	E	E	E	E	E	E	E	E
E	E	E	I	I	I	I	I	I
I	I	I	O	O	O	O	O	O
O	O	U	U	U	U	U	U	
B	B	C	C	D	D	D	D	D
F	F	G	G	G	H	H	J	K
L	L	L	L	M	M	M	N	N
N	N	N	N	P	P	Q	R	R
R	R	R	R	R	S	S	S	S
T	T	T	T	T	T	V	V	V
W	W	W	X	Y	Y	Y	Y	Z
A	B	C	D	E	F	G	H	I
J	K	L	M	N	O	P	Q	R
S	T	U	V	W	X	Y	Z	

READY-TO-USE SPINNER

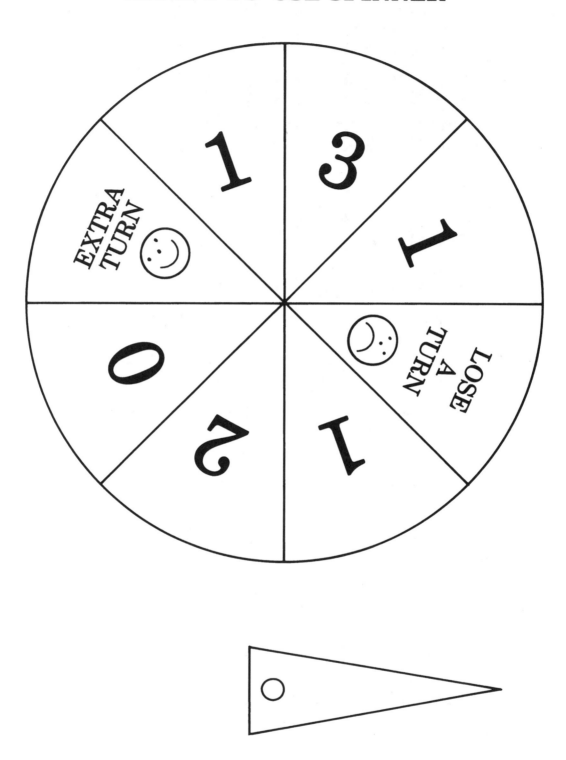

Punch out hole and attach to center of spin dial.

GENERIC SPINNER

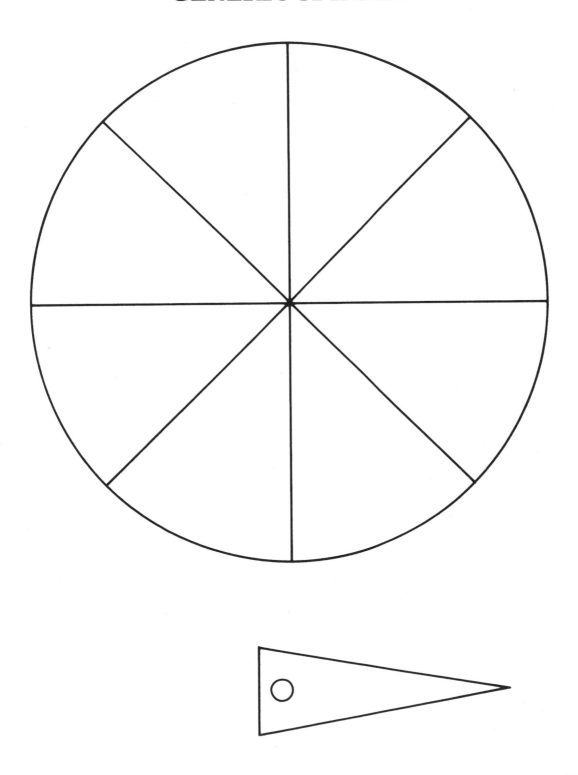

Punch out hole and attach to center of spin dial with paper fastener. Fill in partitions to suit game or other purpose.

Appendix Two

FOR THE TEACHER ONLY

HELPFUL HINTS

You are encouraged to change and modify any of the word puzzles and games. For every example in this book, there are myriads of others you or your students will invent. Students are especially creative when it comes to playing games, often coming up with new rules and procedures that enhance the fun or instructiveness. For instance, the four-team CONTRACTION RELAY, practicing contractions, could easily be adapted to other subject matter. Once children know the basic game, you can substitute almost any topic.

Adaptions should also be made, of course, to account for varying ability levels and time constraints. You can accomplish this by reducing or adding to the number of items, changing content level, and changing instructions to simplify or complicate the game. In lower grades and with less-able pupils you may prefer to read instructions and/or the words themselves or give "clues" by putting answers on the chalkboard from which the students choose the correct answers.

General Pointers for Group Games:

1. For board or other games with small groups, instruct students to take turns in a clockwise direction (next is the person on the student's right). This uniform direction saves confusion and time in getting students accustomed to different games.

2. Games involving strategy or skill, in addition to random luck, hold interest better than luck-only activities. Games involving ONLY strategy or skill are challenging for able students, but discourage less-able ones.

3. Basic materials needed in room for board games: race-type boards, graph paper, 3″ × 5″ blank index cards, dice, marbles, spinners, cards, and squared boards of various sizes.

   Spinners: yes-no, numbers, blank, cardboard arrows
   Cards: letters, blank, numbers, regular playing cards
   Boards: 3″ × 3″, 4″ × 4″, 6″ × 6″, 7″ × 7″, checkerboard

4. **Making Dice**: You can take dice and paste other items over them as needed (such as various colors of paper, different numbers, letters ABCDEF). You can make dice on paper, and use with pips or real numbers. Fold to form a cube and use transparent tape to secure. This is how your pattern should look.

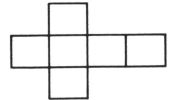
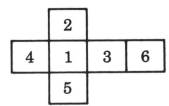

Appendix Three

Teacher Notes for N-1 Through N-22

TEACHER NOTES N-1 THROUGH N-22

N-1 GIVE ME AN <u>A</u> THROUGH GIVE ME A <u>Z</u>: The words used in this original alphabet book are based *as much as possible* on vocabulary lists found in reading and spelling books of major publishers. The reading levels range from reading readiness through second grade. Obviously, some fudging was necessary, as uncommon letters often have less common words.

The illustrations are real and imaginary creatures taken from collections of art works (tapestries, sculptures, cave paintings, etc.) from B.C. through the 20th century. A sharp student may recognize some of them as creatures with other names, though many have been altered to form new creatures.

N-2 PICK UP THE TAIL: This is a written activity, but you can use the same idea for an oral game. If done orally, pick a category. Then call on a student to say a word that fits in the category. The student then calls on another student to "pick up the tail" and give a word beginning with the ending letter of the former student's word. Continue as long as students can answer; then begin again with another word. Change category as needed or save new category for a different day. For less-able students (as a written activity), perhaps change the categories or let them choose just ONE category.

N-3 MOTHER GOOSE AND FRIENDS: I wouldn't count it wrong if students fail to use capital letters on Blue and Peep, but it would be a good chance to explain why they would be capitalized as names. (Perhaps many students will use capital letters throughout the puzzle so it may become a moot question; but if they fill in the blanks, it may become something to point out.)

N-4 RHYME TIME WORD SEARCH: Words are from grades 1–3 spelling lists, though the word search is appropriate for upper elementary students because of its number of items and words spelled backward.

N-5 WHAT LETTERS DO YOU NEED TO ADD? (Parts I, II, III, IV): These words are taken from spelling lists geared for first and second grades. The page looks like a much more formidable task than it is. Essentially, children just practice printing four letters over and over after they figure out which letter goes with each column.

N-6 JUST THREE-LETTER WORDS: This activity can easily be done in partnerships or groups. Each partnership can compete against other partnerships for the whole list, or each partnership can be assigned one column to see who fills the column first.

A table or row can form a group (five groups) and each group can be assigned one column. The group that finishes first is the winner. It is a good idea to have someone from the group read the words to the class, so others can see what words they overlooked. Groups can be assigned the whole list, depending on time available and skill level.

N-7 DROPSY I: This puzzle is suitable for first graders. Words are from grade 1 spelling lists and the action is repetitious.

N-8 DROPSY II: This puzzle is suitable for second half of grade 1. Words are from grade 1 spelling words and the action is repetitious.

N-9 THREE BAGGERS: This puzzle should be suitable for grade level 2. Words are taken from grade 2 spelling lists.

N-10 FOUR BAGGERS: This puzzle should be suitable for grade level 2. Words are taken from grade 2 spelling lists.

N-11 TWO BY FOUR: The following words may be unfamiliar to your age group: don; fore; tam. This is a good opportunity to build general vocabulary with a discussion of these new words while showing how consonants added to the beginnings change words and a final *e* often makes the earlier vowel long. Point out the exception to the rule: *done*.

N-12 SPELLING MAZE: This is not a "made-up" list of spelling words. These words were taken directly from the writings of elementary students, and the misspellings are identical to the way students often spell the words.

N-13 FLOWER POWER: Most suitable for grades 1 and 2.

N-14 STAR POWER: Most suitable for grades 3 and up.

N-15 ANY MONTH FUN: This word game can also be used as a relay with students passing the sheet back along a row or around the table to see which team can find one word for each letter of the month the fastest. Give one point for each word correctly spelled to determine the winning team.

Another variation is to choose groups and have the group come up with as many words beginning with the month's letters as they can. Assign one point for each correctly spelled word. In this latter variation, a time limit should be given. The time will depend on the age and skill level of the class.

N-16 MEMORY RECALL: You can use any familiar words, but this is a great way to review words on spelling lists. Besides spelling practice, it sharpens memory and attention span. Example of a list for younger students: *as; ask; am; at; all*. Older students: *chapter; confuse; custody; customer; complain*.

A variation of this is to have students make up their own lists and read them (twice) to the class, having their classmates try to recall and write down the words. Award points for each word correctly remembered.

Still another variation is to do the memory word game orally with no points to see who can remember the whole list. It is usually best to dispense with the spelling and just have them recite the words or the game gets bogged down. The advantage to this variation is that you usually have time to go through more word lists, but the disadvantage is that, though their memories get a workout, they don't get any spelling practice.

N-17 FOLD IT/PASS IT ON: This routine continues until the end of the row or around the table or prescribed group. About 6–10 players are best. **Rules**: First letter must be a vowel; others must be consonants. All papers are returned to the person whose name is on the sheet. Each person tries to make as many words as possible from the letter on his or her sheet within a given time period.

With older students, no 1-letter or 2-letter words count. Rules can vary with age level. More letters make it easier to form the most words. You may want to have students put two letters per turn if your groups are too small to provide enough letters.

One way to score: 3-letter words (1 point); 4-letter words (2 points); 5-letter words (5 points); words with more than 5 letters (10 points).

N-18 TEAMS: Having students choose teams is risky. Less-able students are not picked to the last and feel left out; students tend to pick their friends, and teams often become unbalanced in skill levels or unruly. Teacher-picked teams are more balanced, but students are sometimes suspicious and resentful having the deck stacked by an adult.

Choosing random teams usually works better. The following simple methods work quickly and effectively: (a) Each student counts and recounts down rows or around tables, depending on number of teams desired (1,2,1,2 for two teams; 1,2,3,4,1,2,3,4 for four teams), and students with the same numbers form each team; (b) each row or table is a team; (c) students pull numbers out of a hat or box to see what team they are on.

N-19 CONTRACTION RELAY: Usually four teams of six players each is about right for this relay. Fortunately, however, uneven numbers on a team can play just as easily as even numbers (some players just get more turns!) See also N-18 on choosing teams.

N-20 M IS FOR MATH: If needed, the words can be put on the board for students to choose from (not in order, of course).

N-21 SPINNERS: Copy the spin dial and spinner (from patterns in Appendix One) on tagboard and laminate them. If you wish, you could use plastic transparency materials. These methods will result in a more durable and easier-to-use spin dial. Attach spinner to dial with a paper-fastening brad, making sure spinner is free to spin easily. Color with felt pen or use with names of colors on dial.

N-22 MARKERS: *Suggested markers or tokens for board games*: beans, pennies, bottle caps, matches (with fire-ends broken off), shells, toothpicks, stones, beads, poker chips, unshelled nuts. Students can bring in markers. (Bottle tops are especially easy to collect.) Store the pieces or tokens for board games in see-through plastic baggies with zipper tops. These can be punched with a paper punch so they can be hung on separate nails or hooks in a closet, back of door, or other convenient storage area.

If pieces or tokens for board games need to be used, taken off the board, and reused during the game, egg cartons can be sliced to size needed for desired number of categories.

Appendix Four

ANSWER KEY

ANSWER KEY

SECTION ONE: READING AND LIBRARY

1–1 Letter Discrimination: A, B, C, D, E, F, G, H, I, J, K, L, M, N, O, P, Q, R, S, T, U, V, W, X, Y, Z.

1–2 Alphabet Connection:

A	B	C	A	D	E	F
L	K	B	J	I	H	G
M	N	C	O	E	P	Q
V	U	T	D	S	F	R
W	X	Y	Z	G	A	C
E	G	I	I	H	K	M
O	Q	J	S	U	W	L
Y	B	D	K	F	H	J
L	N	P	L	R	T	V
X	N	M	Z	B	C	D
J	O	I	H	G	F	E
K	L	P	M	R	N	O
A	S	W	Q	C	S	B
V	C	X	M	T	O	Y
Q	W	E	U	R	T	P
A	S	V	D	F	G	H
Z	R	W	C	V	B	N
P	X	O	I	U	Y	T
Y	A	D	G	J	L	M
M	Z	N	B	V	C	Z

1–3 Qwerty Alphabits: *Top Row*: A, B, C, D, E, F, G, H, I, J; *Middle Row*: K, L, M, N, O, P, Q, R, S; *Bottom Row*: T, U, V, W, X, Y, Z.

1–4 Alphabet Scramble: 1. H (throw); 2. Q (quit); 3. E (game); 4. W (wing); 5. L (block); 6. A (act); 7. V (love); 8. P (map); 9. G (dog); 10. U (club); 11. J (jump); 12. Y (boys); 13. B (bike); 14. K (make); 15. D (side); 16. R (rose); 17. M (room); 18. S (bus); 19. C (luck); 20. X (boxes); 21. F (off); 22. T (pet); 23. I (his); 24. Z (buzz); 25. N (mine); 26. O (bone).

1–5 Give Me an A: ants, anthills.

1–6 Give Me a <u>B</u>: bugs; bushes.

1–7 Give Me a <u>C</u>: cake; caves.

1–8 Give Me a <u>D</u>: dirt; desks.

1–9 Give Me an <u>E</u>: eggs; elms.

1–10 Give Me an <u>F</u>: figs; forests.

1–11 Give Me a <u>G</u>: grapes; gates.

1–12 Give Me an <u>H</u>: hay; holes.

1–13 Give Me an <u>I</u>: insects; India.

1–14 Give Me a <u>J</u>: juice; jeans.

1–15 Give Me a <u>K</u>: kale; kitchens.

1–16 Give Me an <u>L</u>: lions; lakes.

1–17 Give Me an <u>M</u>: moths; mountains.

1–18 Give Me an <u>N</u>: notebooks; nests.

1–19 Give Me an <u>O</u>: olives; octopuses.

1–20 Give Me a <u>P</u>: pancakes; puddles.

1–21 Give Me a <u>Q</u>: quail; quilts.

1–22 Give Me an <u>R</u>: roses; rocks.

1–23 Give Me an <u>S</u>: seeds; soil.

1–24 Give Me a <u>T</u>: toads; tugboats.

1–25 Give Me a <u>U</u>: uncles; umbrellas.

1–26 Give Me a <u>V</u>: varmints; vans.

1–27 Give Me a <u>W</u>: worms; wells.

1–28 Give Me an <u>X</u>: xenon; Xanthus.

1–29 Give Me a <u>Y</u>: yarn; yards.

1–30 Give Me a <u>Z</u>: zippers; zoos.

1–31 Pairs O' Shoes: 1. (ch) chin/chop; 2. (cl) clown/club; 3. (cr) criss/cross; 4. (sl) slow/slam; 5. (sm) small/smile; 6. (st) stop/street; 7. (dr) drip/drop; 8. (wh) white/whale.

1–32 Boxed Pairs: *Can be in any order.* 1. (th) thank/them; 2. (sh) short/ship; 3. (gl) glad/glass; 4. (gr) green/grass; 5. (sn) snip/snap; 6. (br) brown/brick; 7. (bl) black/blend; 8. (fr) frog/frown; 9. (fl) flag/flew.

1–33 <u>SH</u> Sounds: *Answers can be in any order.* 1. shop; 2. she; 3. show; 4. short; 5. shore; 6. shine.

1–34 <u>TH</u> Sounds: 1. mouth; 2. path; 3. with; 4. three; 5. teeth; 6. thanks; 7. thirst; 8. both; 9. north; 10. thick; 11. moth; 12. Thursday.

1–35 Silent Consonants: 1. light; 2. climb; 3. walk; 4. lamb; 5. night; 6. castle; 7. sigh; 8. thumb.

1–36 Short Vowel Sounds: *Answers can be in any order.* 1. up; 2. fit; 3. cat; 4. ask; 5. lot; 6. well.

1–37 Silent Letters: 1. know; 2. high; 3. should; 4. who; 5. game; 6. night. *Student answers are the first and last letters of these words. Circled silent letters are underlined here.*

1–38 Silly Paragraph (final E): 1. fine; 2. man; 3. rode; 4. van; 5. hat; 6. white; 7. cane; 8. not; 9. far; 10. Can; 11. code; 12. shine; 13. note; 14. hope; 15. dim; 16. dot.

1–39 Musical Notes: 1. do; 2. re; 3. mi; 4. fa; 5. sol; 6. la; 7. ti; 8. do.

1–40 Silly Syllables: 1. FAN-TA-SY; 2. EN-CY-CLO-PED-I-A; 3. TI-TLE; 4. PLAY-WRIGHT; 5. AU-THOR; 6. BI-OG-RA-PHY; 7. FA-BLE; 8. IN-DEX.

1–41 Test Your Logic: Mario (Italy, Brown); Juan (Mexico, Black); Nigel (England, Red); Hans (Germany, Yellow); Charles (Canada, Grey).

1–42 Sequence: *Paragraph I*: 1. 1; 2. 3; 3. 6; *Paragraph II*: 1. 8; 2. 2; 3. 5; 4. 4; 5. 7.

1–43 Call to Order: 1. C; 2. B; 3. D; 4. A.

1–44 Rows and Columns: GOOD BOOKS.

1–45 Categories: *Answers may vary; here are some possibilities.* 1. months: March, May; foods: melon, mango, meat; states: Maine, Maryland, Massachusetts, Michigan, Minnesota, Mississippi, Missouri, Montana; 2. months: April, August; foods: apple, apricot, asparagus; states: Alabama, Alaska, Arizona, Arkansas; 3. months: October; foods: orange; states: Ohio, Oklahoma, Oregon; 4. months: February; foods: figs; states: Florida; 5. months: September; foods: squash; states: South Carolina, South Dakota.

1–46 Scattergorize: *Answers may be in any order under the category. Animals*: bat, bird, cat, dog, duck, fox, frog, hen, horse, pig; *Colors*: black, blue, brown, grey, green, orange, pink, red, white, yellow; *Numbers*: one, two, three, four, five, six, seven, eight, nine, ten.

1–47 Odd Man Out: 1. I; 2. can; 3. do; 4. good; 5. work. *Sentence*: I can do good work.

1–48 Shapes and Categories: 1. 6 colors in circle: red, blue, purple, black, orange, yellow; 2. 5 numbers in square: 3, 4, 5, 6, 10; 3. 3 months in triangle: June, March, July.

1–49 Instrument Families: *Strings (any order)*: 1. harp; 2. violin; 3. viola; 4. cello; 5. bass; 6. piano. *Winds (any order)*: 7. oboe; 8. clarinet; 9. English horn; 10. bassoon; 11. flute; 12. piccolo; 13. trumpet; 14. French horn; 15. trombone; 16. tuba; 17. saxophone. *Percussion (any order)*: 18. chimes; 19. glockenspiel; 20. triangle; 21. cymbals; 22. drums; 23. xylophone.

1–50 Categories: Bigger and Bigger: 1. apple; 2. fruit; 3. agriculture; 4. Chevrolet; 5. automobile; 6. transportation; 7. cellular phone; 8. telephone; 9. communication; 10. goldfish; 11. fish; 12. aquarium; 13. Red Sox; 14. baseball; 15. summer sports; 16. Senate; 17. democracy; 18. government; 19. puck; 20. ice hockey; 21. winter sports; 22. stamps; 23. collections; 24. hobbies; 25. clarinet; 26. orchestra; 27. music.

1–51 Pick Up the Tail: *Answers will vary.*

1–52 What Part of a Book Am I?: 1. cover; 2. spine; 3. title; 4. author; 5. illustrator.

1–53 Nursery Rhyme Puzzle: 1. Farmer in the Dell; 2. I Saw Three Ships; 3. The Queen of Hearts; 4. Humpty Dumpty; 5. Jack Jump Over the Candlestick; 6. Simple Simon; 7. Georgie Porgie; 8. Three Little Kittens.

1–54 Mother Goose and Friends: *Across*: 1. lamb; 3. wall; 5. time; 6. lion; 7. plum; 9. dock; 11. pipe; 12. none. *Down*: 1. lost; 2. Blue; 3. wool; 4. lean; 7. Peep; 8. mice; 9. down; 10. knee.

1–55 Little Ones (Easy): 1. Bo Peep; 2. Jack Horner; 3. Women; 4. Men; 5. House on the Prairie; 6. Red Riding Hood; 7. Miss Muffet; 8. Boy Blue; 9. Tommy Tucker; 10. John.

1–56 Little Ones (Harder): 1. Prince; 2. Pigs; 3. Chicken; 4. House in the Big Woods; 5. Molly Flinders; 6. Stuart; 7. Robin Redbreast; 8. Boy Lost; 9. White Horse; 10. Red Hen; 11. Princess; 12. Engine That Could.

1–57 Book or Story Titles: 1. Little Women; 2. Snow White and the Seven Dwarfs; 3. Little House in the Big Woods; 4. The Cat in the Hat; 5. Where the Sidewalk Ends; 6. Charlotte's Web; 7. The Trumpet of the Swan; 8. Tulips and Chimneys; 9. The Four Million; 10. Lord of the Rings.

1–58 Story Fun: 1. Rey; 2. dog; 3. egg; 4. Oz; 5. ham. *Puzzle Word*: smarty.

1–59 Count Your Reading: 1. One; 2. Two; 3. Three; 4. Four; 5. Five; 6. Six; 7. Seven; 8. Eight; 9. Nine; 10. Ten. *Sentence under picture*: This is called a hole in ONE.

1–60 Reds Are Read: 1. Red; 2. Red; 3. Red; 4. Scarlet; 5. Red; 6. Red; 7. Scarlet; 8. Red; 9. Red; 10. Scarlet; 11. Red; 12. Red; 13. Red; 14. Scarlet(t).

1–61 What Character Am I?: *Characters and clues will vary.*

1–62 Animal Characters Outline: *I. Dogs*: (A. Big Red; B. Clifford; C. Ribsy; D. White Fang); *II. Bears*: (A. Berenstain; B. Gentle Ben; C. Paddington; D. Winnie-the-Pooh); *III. Cats*: (A. Cat in the Hat; B. Garfield; C. Puss-in-Boots; D. Socks); *IV. Horses*: (A. Black Beauty; B. Flicka; C. Misty; D. Stormy).

1–63 Color the Rhyme: 1. sand/band/hand; 2. had/bad/sad; 3. bike/hike/pike; 4. cross or plus sign.

1–64 Easy Rhyming Pairs: 1. six/fix; 2. west/test; 3. eggs/legs; 4. spring/string; 5. chair/pair; 6. kittens/mittens; 7. loose/goose; 8. pen/men.

1–65 Rhyme Time Word Search: *Words in word search puzzle under each heading are POP*: drop; stop; crop; mop; cop; hop; top; *ROCK*: flock; lock; clock; mock; sock; dock; frock; *BAND*: hand; and; sand; grand; land; stand; strand. *Non-rhyming words in the puzzle are incorrect answers.*

1–66 Do You Understand the Dictionary?: Can you read these words using dictionary symbols? It is good practice to try it. Copy the real words on the lines below.

1–67 Fiction Versus Nonfiction: 1. R; 2. T; 3. E; 4. G; 5. A. *Letters unscrambled spell* GREAT.

1–68 Proverb Nit-Picking: 1. 4; 2. 9 *(last proverb in this set has 5 syllables so 4 + 5 = 9)*; 3. 9 *(first and third proverb in this set have 9 syllables)*; 4. 6; 5. 18; 6. 12 *(18 − 6)*; 7. 2 *(4 − 2)*; 8. 2 *(not and handsome)*. *Computation at bottom*: 4 + 9 = 9 + 6 − 2 *(13 = 13)*; 18 − 12 = 2 + 2 + 2 *(6 = 6)*.

1–69 Dictionary Guide Words Race: *Guide words will vary depending on dictionaries used.*

SECTION TWO: SPELLING AND VOCABULARY

2–1 Color Stretch:

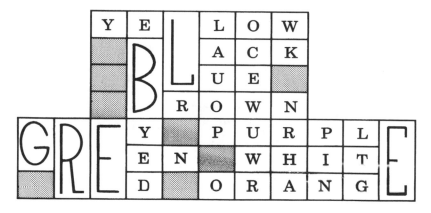

246

2–2 Mix and Match Colors: 1. Red; 2. Yellow; 3. Blue; 4. Orange; 5. Green; 6. Purple.

2–3 Shape Words: 1. circle; 2. rectangle; 3. triangle; 4. oval; 5. square.

2–4 A Dear Tale or A Deer Tail?: 1. Here; 2. our; 3. tale; 4. deer; 5. tail; 6. hear; 7. meet; 8. our; 9. dear; 10. there; 11. Hour; 12. hour; 13. deer; 14. for; 15. our; 16. scent; 17. its; 18. way.

2–5 Bare/Bear Puzzle: *Across*: 1. bear; 2. bare; 3. bare; 4. bare; 5. bare; 6. bear; 7. bear; 8. bear; 9. bear. *Down*: 1. bear; 2. bear; 3. bear; 5. bear; 6. bare; 7. bare; 8. bare.

2–6 Drop-a-Letter Sound-Alikes: 1. be; 2. new; 3. our; 4. we; 5. or; 6. to; 7. not; 8. night.

2–7 Homonyms the Easy Way: 1. ring; 2. main; 3. hole; 4. burro; 5. rap; 6. by; 7. new; 8. cent; 9. ad; 10. so.

2–8 "B" Words That Lead a Double Life: a. band; b. bore; c. box; d. bill; e. bat; f. break; g. bear; h. bowl; i. bluff; j. brush; k. bark; l. boil.

2–9 Homographs: *Stories will vary.*

2–10 Reverse It: 1. ten; 2. saw; 3. ton; 4. top; 5. tog; 6. no; 7. sub; 8. tub; 9. gut; 10. pets; 11. peak; 12. stop; 13. tops; 14. tea; 15. won; 16. rats; 17. team; 18. rub.

2–11 Backward and Forward Spelling: 1. mom; 2. pep; 3. sis; 4. pup; 5. pop; 6. eye; 7. dad; 8. did; 9. noon; 10. toot; 11. peep.

2–12 The Other Side of the Coin: 1. down; 2. day; 3. in; 4. before; 5. black; 6. south; 7. under; 8. below; 9. top; 10. summer; 11. ten cents; 12. fifty cents; 13. one dollar.

2–13 Same and Opposite Anagrams: *Across*: 1. alone; 2. diner; 3. eight; 4. clown; 5. lady; 6. throw; 7. gold. *Down*: 1. uncle; 2. soft; 3. bad; 4. warm; 5. rich; 6. found; 7. quiet.

2–14 End Sounds: 1. cobra; 2. cab; 3. disc; 4. red; 5. tepee; 6. off; 7. leg; 8. brush; 9. alibi; 10. dj; 11. clock; 12. reel; 13. roam; 14. man; 15. auto; 16. ship; 17. Iraq; 18. actor; 19. atlas; 20. part; 21. haiku; 22. rev; 23. meow; 24. ox; 25. key; 26. jazz.

2–15 Do You Like Art?: 1. cart; 2. dart; 3. part; 4. tart; 5. wart; 6. chart; 7. heart; 8. quart; 9. smart; 10. start; 11. earth; 12. party.

2–16 Related Words: 1. snow–ball–game; 2. note–book–case; 3. bath–room–mate; 4. hunt–club–soda; 5. plum–tree–tops; 6. lake–side–show; 7. life–time–line; 8. home–work–shop; 9. down–town–ship.

2–17 Compound Words: *There is more than one solution. Count them correct if all words connected by lines are in fact compound words. One solution:* (*2nd row*) bird; out; top. (*last row*) seed; house; fit; side; heavy. (*compound words*) blackbird; blackout; blacktop; birdseed; birdhouse; outhouse; outfit; outside; topside; topheavy.

2–18 Compound Train Cars: 1. wrist/dog (wristwatch; watchdog); 2. bare/track (bareback; backtrack); 3. wood/lady (woodland; landlady); 4. ball/mate (ballroom; roommate); 5. note/keeper (notebook; bookkeeper); 6. butter/cake (buttercup; cupcake); 7. birth/break (birthday; daybreak).

2–19 Missing Links: Endings: 1. lasting; 2. owning; 3. parting; 4. ending; 5. handing; 6. lasted; 7. owned; 8. parted; 9. ended; 10. handed.

2–20 Prefix and Suffix Kite: (*inside kite, any order*) 1. remix; 2. premix; 3. unmix; (*tail of kite, any order*) 4. mixed; 5. mixing; 6. mixer; 7. mixable; 8. mixes.

2–21 What Letters Do You Need to Add? (Part I): *Column 1 (b)*: 1. be; 2. bee; 3. bed; 4. bit; 5. big; 6. bug; 7. bus; 8. but; 9. best; 10. bike; 11. bite; 12. bone. *Column 2 (l)*: 1. let; 2. leg; 3. lot; 4. law; 5. low; 6. look; 7. long; 8. lake; 9. like; 10. left; 11. line; 12. lost. *Column 3 (p)*: 1. pen; 2. pet; 3.

pig; 4. pan; 5. pop; 6. pin; 7. pat; 8. plum; 9. pole; 10. pond; 11. pipe; 12. part. *Column 4 (f)*: 1. fox; 2. fun; 3. fan; 4. fog; 5. fry; 6. fly; 7. for; 8. frog; 9. fast; 10. four; 11. farm; 12. feet.

2–22 What Letters Do You Need to Add? (Part II): *Column 1 (c)*: 1. can; 2. cat; 3. cut; 4. cap; 5. cot; 6. cup; 7. car; 8. cow; 9. came; 10. call; 11. clap; 12. coat. *Column 2 (j)*: 1. jet; 2. job; 3. jug; 4. jab; 5. jay; 6. jut; 7. jar; 8. jam; 9. jot; 10. joke; 11. jump; 12. just. *Column 3 (t)*: 1. to; 2. top; 3. tub; 4. try; 5. two; 6. ten; 7. tree; 8. take; 9. time; 10. talk; 11. tape; 12. told. *Column 4 (g)*: 1. go; 2. get; 3. got; 4. gun; 5. grow; 6. give; 7. grey; 8. game; 9. gate; 10. gave; 11. good; 12. girl.

2–23 What Letters Do You Need to Add? (Part III): *Column 1 (d)*: 1. do; 2. dad; 3. did; 4. dot; 5. dog; 6. day; 7. dig; 8. dry; 9. dark; 10. dust; 11. duck; 12. dish. *Column 2 (h)*: 1. he; 2. had; 3. hat; 4. has; 5. his; 6. him; 7. hot; 8. hop; 9. hug; 10. hike; 11. home; 12. hope. *Column 3 (r)*: 1. ran; 2. red; 3. run; 4. rug; 5. ring; 6. rode; 7. room; 8. rest; 9. rock; 10. rake; 11. ride; 12. rope. *Column 4 (k)*: 1. kit; 2. key; 3. kid; 4. kin; 5. kiss; 6. kind; 7. kick; 8. keep; 9. kite; 10. kilt; 11. king; 12. kitten.

2–24 What Letters Do You Need to Add? (Part IV): *Column 1 (w)*: 1. win; 2. was; 3. week; 4. walk; 5. will; 6. went; 7. wave; 8. want; 9. wait; 10. wish; 11. with; 12. well. *Column 2 (n)*: 1. no; 2. net; 3. not; 4. now; 5. nod; 6. new; 7. noon; 8. nine; 9. name; 10. nose; 11. need; 12. nice. *Column 3 (s)*: 1. set; 2. sea; 3. sun; 4. see; 5. safe; 6. soon; 7. seed; 8. slam; 9. same; 10. side; 11. save; 12. still. *Column 4 (m)*: 1. man; 2. met; 3. mom; 4. may; 5. mop; 6. map; 7. mud; 8. must; 9. made; 10. mine; 11. milk; 12. mule.

2–25 As Easy As 1-2-3: (*Set 1*) 1. me; 2. man; 3. many. (*Set 2*) 1. hi; 2. her; 3. high; 4. house. (*Set 3*) 1. we; 2. war; 3. work; 4. water; 5. wanted.

2–26 Just Three-Letter Words: *Answers will vary. Here are some possibilities.* **at**: bat; cat; fat; gat; hat; mat; pat; rat; sat; tat; vat. **et**: bet; get; jet; let; met; net; pet; set; vet; wet; yet. **it**: bit; fit; hit; kit; lit; mit; nit; pit; sit; tit; wit; zit. **ot**: cot; dot; got; hot; jot; lot; not; pot; rot; sot; tot. **ut**: but; cut; gut; hut; jut; nut; put; rut; tut.

2–27 Three-Baggers: 1. when/hen/he; 2. fork/for/or; 3. bush/bus/us; 4. them/hem/he (*or*) them/the/he; 5. beef/bee/be; 6. took/too/to; 7. good/goo/go; 8. done/one/on (*or*) done/don/on; 8. does/doe/do; 10. small/mall/all; 11. week/wee/we; 12. been/bee/be; 13. fine/fin/in; 14. wind/win/in.

2–28 Dropsy I: 1. an; 2. it; 3. at; 4. he; 5. am; 6. as; 7. us; 8. is.

2–29 Dropsy II: 1. see; 2. fee; 3. not; 4. hop; 5. rid; 6. bit; 7. hid; 8. rod.

2–30 Four-Baggers: 1. bath/bat/at/a; 2. with/wit/it/I; 3. this/his/is/I; 4. bite/bit/it/I; 5. store/tore/ore/or; 6. wing/win/in/I.

2–31 A Fine Kettle of Fish: 1. man; 2. walked; 3. with; 4. baskets; 5. full; 6. will; 7. tell; 8. you; 9. right; 10. said; 11. fry; 12. fine; 13. kettle; 14. fish.

2–32 Anagram Ladders: 1. mat/tame; 2. rod/door; 3. tip/spit; 4. use/sure (*or*) sue/ruse; 5. nap/pain; 6. sit/stir. *There may be other solutions.*

2–33 Add-A-Letter Anagrams: *There are many answers. Some possible answers*: a/an/ant/pant/paint; a/an/and/wand/wands; a/at/ate/date/dates; a/at/ate/hate/hated; I/it/sit/site/spite; I/in/pin/pine/spine; I/is/his/sigh/sighs; I/if/fin/fine/fined.

2–34 Let's Go to the Circus: 1. o; 2. e/a/u; 3. e/e/a; 4. o/e; 5. u/e; 6. e/o/a/e; 7. e/a; 8. a/o/a; 9. a/o/o; 10. o/o/a; 11. i/o/a/e.

2–35 Missing Vowel Petals (A, E, I, O, U): 1. pansy; 2. tulip; 3. peony; 4. iris; 5. daisy.

2–36 The Case of the Missing Vowels: 1. A (can, man, dad, had, ran); 2. E (met, men, get, yes, let); 3. I (did, him, bit, big, sit); 4. O (mom, job, top, hot, dot); 5. U (sun, nut, hug, run, cup). *Five vowels*: A, E, I, O, U.

2–37 Two By Four: 1. at; mat; mate; 2. in; pin; pine; 3. an; can; cane; 4. on; don; done; 5. it; kit; kite; 6. or; for; fore; 7. am; tam; tame.

2–38 Plus and Minus: 1. desk; 2. test; 3. globe; 4. learn; 5. write; 6. lesson; 7. class; 8. child. *Words are related to: SCHOOL.*

2–39 Word Play: 1. buy; 2. grid; 3. men; 4. lacy; 5. fine.

2–40 Code Clues: 1. boy; 2. cat; 3. dog; 4. girl.

2–41 Find the Common Letters: 1. g; 2. r; 3. e; 4. a; 5. t. *Word*: GREAT.

2–42 Two-Letter Word Blocks: I. (*Across*) an/so; (*Down*) as/no. II. (*Across*) oh/we; (*Down*) ow/he.

2–43 Little Words Get Bigger: 1. the/they; 2. his/this; 3. ore/more; 4. hem/them; 5. doe/does; 6. hen/then; 7. ade/made; 8. fin/find; 9. man/many; 10. now/know; 11. too/took; 12. goo/good.

2–44 Little Words Get Smaller: 1. hat/at; 2. and/an; 3. wit/it; 4. his/is; 5. bee/be; 6. tan/an; 7. ram/am; 8. hen/he; 9. her/he; 10. own/on; 11. one/on; 12. our/or.

2–45 Spider Web Spelling: *Answers will vary. Some of the words that can be formed*: mat; mate; mole; mop; lop; lope; let; map; pat; tap; pet; tape; mope; at; am; tam.

2–46 Backwards Spelling: *Grade 3*: 1. balloon; 2. lunch; 3. cuff; 4. dull; 5. sled; 6. plot; 7. drop; 8. land; 9. plan; 10. last. *Grade 2*: 1. long; 2. cute; 3. does; 4. cup; 5. win; 6. next; 7. hand; 8. fan. *Grade 1*: 1. you; 2. she; 3. are; 4. the; 5. at.

2–47 Spelling Maze: *The following words are misspelled*: 1. bu*sy*; 2. f*i*rst; 3. pr*e*tty; 4. p*ie*ce; 5. ve*ry*.

2–48 Double L Words: 1. collie; 2. gallop; 3. teller; 4. ballad; 5. dollar; 6. killer; 7. follow; 8. pollen; 9. gallon; 10. ballot. *Circled letters spell*: GREAT.

2–49 Double Oh Oh Seven: 1. wool; 2. foot; 3. root; 4. food; 5. noon; 6. book; 7. good. *The word spelled the same forward and backward*: NOON.

2–50 Look Over the Four-Leaf Clover: *Some of the words possible*: ten; set; net; steno; toe; one; note; nest; tone; nose; sent. *The 5-letter bonus word*: STONE.

2–51 Flower Power: *Some of the words possible*: pan; tan; an; pal; pad; lad; tad; date; ate; pate; late; neat; eat; peat; leap; lead; nape; ale; pale; dale; tale; pat; at; and; land; pedal; pant; ant; pane; lane; dane; ape; ade; teal; peal; deal; dean; lean; lap; nap; tap; tape. *The 7-letter word*: PLANTED.

2–52 Star Power: *Some of the words possible*: asp; least; teal; peat; seal; seat; peal; leap; steal; late; eat; paste; ate; pate; late; tap; tape; ape; lap; lapse; sap; tale; sale; sat; pat; pal; pale; ale; salt; last; past; pea; sea; lea; tea; slat; slate. *The 6-letter word*: PASTEL.

2–53 Word Scramble Secret: 1. (c)orn; 2. smi(l)e; 3. f(o)rk; 4. dr(u)m; 5. ban(d). *Secret word*: CLOUD.

2–54 Months and Holidays: 1. December; 2. October; 3. January; 4. September; 5. March; 6. August; 7. November; 8. February; 9. July; 10. June; 11. May; 12. April.

2–55 Word Origins of Months and Days of Week: *1st column*: June, October, Saturday, November, February, Friday, Thursday, August, July, Wednesday; *2nd column*: Monday,

Sunday, January, September, April, Tuesday, March, December, May; *months of year in order:* January, February, March, April, May, June, July, August, September, October, November, December; *days of week in order:* Sunday, Monday, Tuesday, Wednesday, Thursday, Friday, Saturday.

2–56 Signs of the Times: 1. NC(Y); 2. D(O); 3. D(U); 4. (D)E; 5. (O)P; 6. IN(G); 7. FI(R); 8. TR(E); 9. (A)D; 10. (T)H; 11. BE(W); 12. P(O); 13. (R)ES; 14. L(K). *Circled letters spell:* YOU DO GREAT WORK!

2–57 Sports Match: 1. puck; 2. jab; 3. love; 4. steal; 5. punt; 6. tuck; 7. turf; 8. hoop; 9. tee.

2–58 Ask a Silly Question: 1. maggot; 2. earth; 3. eagle; 4. terrific; 5. yo-yo; 6. oar; 7. unicorn; 8. Abe; 9. teacher. *Answer:* MEET YOU AT THE CORNER.

2–59 Find the Missing Babies: 1. colt; 2. kitten; 3. kid; 4. calf; 5. lamb; 6. fawn; 7. foal; 8. vixen; 9. farrow; 10. cub.

2–60 Fours: *Answers may be in any order within a group of four. Directions:* north/south/east/west; *seasons:* autumn or fall/winter/summer/spring; *human limbs:* right leg/left leg/right arm/left arm; *kinds of sentences:* statement or declarative/question or interrogative/command or imperative/strong emotion or exclamatory.

2–61 Any Month Fun: *Answers will vary depending on month chosen.*

SECTION THREE:
LANGUAGE ARTS, MATHEMATICS, SOCIAL STUDIES, AND SCIENCE

(*Language Arts*)

3–1 Valentine: 1. v/a/l/e/n/t/i/n/e (9); 2. val/en/tine (3); 3. a/e/i/e (4); 4. v/l/n/t/n (5); 5. e/n (2); 6. V (1); 7. a/l/e/n/t/i/n/e (8); 8. v/a/l/e/n/t/i (7); 9. vale/ale/lent/tin/in/tine (6).

3–2 Sentences to Divide and Conquer: 1. Wednesday is a day of the week; 2. February is the second month of the year; 3. Fall and autumn are the same season; 4. Summer is hot; 5. Red and blue are colors.

3–3 Sentence Sense: *Sentences and punctuation needed:* 1. period; 5. period; 7. exclamation point; 8. period; 10. question mark. *Secret word scrambled:* AERGT; *Secret word unscrambled:* GREAT.

3–4 Mercedes, the Cat: 1. Mercedes; 2. sleek; 3. spunky; 4. trouble; 5. counter; 6. laundry; 7. way; 8. it.

3–5 Punctuation Riddles: 1. question mark (?); 2. period (.); 3. comma (,); 4. exclamation mark (!); 5. quotation marks (" ").

3–6 Contractions Detective: 1. o (does not); 2. o (do not); 3. o (had not); 4. i (he is); 5. i (here is); 6. a (I am); 7. o (is not); 8. i (she is); 9. i (that is); 10. i (there is); 11. i (what is); 12. i (who is).

3–7 Changing Nouns With T: 1. train; 2. tone; 3. tape; 4. tear; 5. tale; 6. twin; 7. tire; 8. tax; 9. trail; 10. trash.

3–8 Noun–Verb Words: *Paragraphs will vary.*

3–9 Plural Tic-Tac-Toe: deer; men; pigs.

3–10 Contraction Relay: *Answers will vary. Possibilities:* can't; won't; shan't; didn't; don't; doesn't; ain't (*yes, it's in the dictionary!*); wouldn't; shouldn't; couldn't; would've; should've; could've; isn't; aren't; wasn't; weren't; hasn't; haven't; hadn't; you'd; I'd; we'd; they'd; he'd; she'd; it'd; mightn't; might've; I'm; you're; we're; they're; who're; he's; she's; it's; what's; that's; who's; who've; there's; there've; here's; one's; there'd; what'd; who'd; that'd; I've; you've; we've; they've; I'll; you'll; she'll; he'll; it'll; we'll; they'll; this'll; that'll; these'll; those'll; there'll; who'll; what'll.

(*Mathematics*)

3–16 M Is for Math: 1. minus; 2. most; 3. metric; 4. minute; 5. match; 6. meter; 7. multiply; 8. measure; 9. middle; 10. mean. *Bottom of page:* THERE ARE 18 CLIMBERS.

3–17 Easy Math Progressions: 1. 4; 2. 6; 3. 16; 4. 16; 5. 20; 6. 12; 7. 400; 8. 6; 9. 16. *Code letters (xleecntle) unscramble to* EXCELLENT.

3–18 Shortcuts: 1. 2 cups in a pint; 2. 2 pints in a quart; 3. 4 quarts in a gallon; 4. 8 ounces in a cup; 5. 16 tablespoons in a cup; 6. 12 months in a year; 7. 7 days in a week; 8. 52 weeks in a year; 9. 365 days in a year; 10. 60 seconds in a minute; 11. 60 minutes in an hour; 12. 24 hours in a day; 13. 12 inches in a foot; 14. 3 feet in a yard; 15. 26 letters in the alphabet.

3–19 What's Next?:

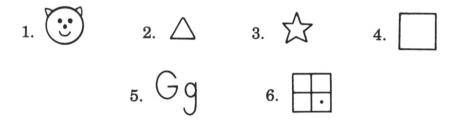

3–20 Spelling with Roman Numerals: 1. five; 2. cold; 3. lid; 4. mix; 5. dim; 6. six; 7. cod.

3–21 Frozen Yogurt Pie Graph: *Graph should show correct information.* 1. peach; 2. 2; 3. *Answers will vary.*

3–22 Holiday Dates: 1. October 7; 2. May 14; 3. June 18; 4. March 17; 5. October 9; 6. February 14; 7. February 2; 8. May 30; 9. December 7; 10. November 11; 11. July 4; 12. January 16; 13. January 1.

3–23 February Fun: A. 12; B. 22; C. 14; D. 2; 1. 10; 2. 8; 3. 14; 4. 16; 5. 50.

3–24 Easy Math Squares: #1. *Across:* 1 + 3 = 4; 4 − 2 = 2. *Down:* 1 + 4 = 5; 3 − 2 = 1; 4 + 2 = 6. #2. *Across:* 2 × 5 = 10; 6 ÷ 3 = 2. *Down:* 2 × 6 = 12; 5 × 3 = 15; 10 ÷ 2 = 5.

3–25 Math Spelling: 1. zero; 2. one; 3. eight; 4. ten; 5. nine; 6. eleven; 7. nine; 8. eight; 9. three; 10. eight; 11. two.

3–26 It All Adds Up: 1. 1; 2. 2; 3. 3; 4. 4; (total = 10); 5. 3; 6. 2; 7. 4; 8. 1; (total = 10).

3–27 Odds and Evens: 1/3/3/7/1/1/5/5/3/1 (1 + 3 = 4; 3 + 3 = 6; 3 + 7 = 10; 7 + 1 = 8; 1 + 1 = 2; 1 + 5 = 6; 5 + 5 = 10; 5 + 3 = 8; 3 + 1 = 4).

3–28 A Few Big States: 2. Arizona; 3. California; 4. Idaho; 5. Montana; 6. Nevada; 7. Oregon; 8. Texas; 9. Utah; 10. Wyoming.

3–29 Career Search: 1. teacher; 2. plumber; 3. electrician; 4. nurse; 5. secretary; 6. postman; 7. pilot; 8. cook.

3–30 People Connections: 1. c; 2. g; 3. d; 4. h; 5. b; 6. i; 7. a; 8. j; 9. f; 10. e.

3–31 President's Day: *Drawing should look like a caricature of Abraham Lincoln holding a scroll with the name ABE on it.*

3–32 Where Would You Be?: 1. England; 2. Germany; 3. United States; 4. Japan; 5. Italy. *Special message:* GREAT.

(*Science*)

3–33 Say What?: *Students may start their lists anywhere as long as the sounds match the animals:* pig/oink; snake/ssss; owl/who; cat/meow; sheep/baa; cow/moo; bird/chirp; dog/arf; donkey/hee-haw.

3–34 Just Call Me a Group!: *Students may start their lists anywhere as long as the groups match the animals:* school/fish; swarm/bees; pod/seals; gaggle/geese; flock/sheep; herd/elephants; bed/clams; colony/ants; pack/wolves; pride/lions.

3–35 Big Ones/Little Ones: 1. kitten; 2. whelp (*puppy is also correct, but it is not in the "little ones" choices*); 3. foal; 4. squab; 5. joey; 6. cygnet.

3–36 Horsing Around: 1. Morgan; 2. Palomino; 3. Shetland; 4. Appaloosa; 5. Clydesdale; 6. Belgian; 7. Percheron; 8. Turk; 9. Arab.

3–37 Animal Appetites: 1. berries; 2. grass (or hay); 3. hay (or grass); 4. fish; 5. cheese; 6. honey.

3–38 Here, Kitty, Kitty: 1. manx; 2. angora; 3. siamese; 4. persian; 5. shorthair; 6. chinchilla.

3–39 Holiday Plants and Animals: I. Christmas; A. reindeer; B. poinsettia; II. Easter; A. bunny; B. lily; III. Halloween; A. cat; B. pumpkin; IV. Thanksgiving; A. turkey; B. cranberries.

3–40 Tropical Ocean Fish: *Words with doubled letters:* barracuda; bass; puffer; snook; wahoo. *Letters doubled:* r; s; f; o; o. *Unscrambled answer to question:* ROOFS.

3–41 Do You Know Your Crustaceans?: 4. shrimp; lobster; barnacle; crab; prawn; ostracod. *The crossed-out ocean fish are:* sailfish; batfish; seahorse; angelfish; goatfish; devilfish; goby; snapper; grouper.

3–42 What Do These Words Have in Common?: *Code letters:* l/l/s/s/e/h; *Code word:* SHELLS.

3–43 Reptiles: 1. all; 2. cod; 3. ham; 4. rag/ago; 5. add; 6. cob/bra; 7. rat; 8. pin/err/rap; 9. art; 10. gam; 11. via; 12. all; 13. con; 14. cop; 15. ace; 16. tar.

3–44 Bugaboo: *Letters form* BUG SPRAY.

3–45 A Busy Woodpecker: 1. e/a (cedar); 2. i (fir); 3. e/o (hemlock); 4. e/o/o (redwood); 5. i/e (pine); 6. u/e (spruce); 7. a (ash); 8. a/e (aspen); 9. a/o/o (basswood); 10. e/e (beech); 11. i (birch); 12. e (cherry); 13. e (elm); 14. u (gum); 15. i/o (hickory); 16. a/e (maple); 17. o/a (oak); 18. u/i (tulip); 19. a/u (walnut); 20. i/o (willow).

3–46 Missed You: 1–8. U; 9. Earth; 10. Mars.

3–47 Water Birds: 1. bat (albatross); 2. boo (booby); 3. ran, ant (cormorant); 4. coo (coot); 5. cur (curlew); 6. bit (bittern); 7. ran (crane); 8. net (gannet); 9. goo (goose); 10. her (heron); 11. kit (kittiwake); 12. all (mallard); 13. can (pelican); 14. pen (penguin); 15. fin (puffin); 16. wan (swan). *Words that have more or fewer than three letters should not be counted as correct. Birds without three-letter words*: 17. auk; 18. grebe; 19. gull; 20. loon; 21. murre; 22. plover; 23. tern; 24. stork.

3–48 Easy-Add-a-Letter Foods: 1. p (pear); 2. o (orange); 3. m (milk); 4. m (meat); 5. p (peach); 6. o (olive); 7. h (ham).

NOTES

NOTES

NOTES

PRIMARY TEACHER'S BOOK OF INSTANT WORD GAMES

Over 190 Ready-to-Use Games and Activities for Any Basal or Whole Language Program!

JUDIE L.H. STROUF

For all teachers in grades K-3, here is an exciting collection of 194 ready-to-use individual word puzzles and group word games based on the essential elements and competencies taught at the primary grade level.

The activities are student-tested and designed to be educationally sound and relevant to the reading/spelling/language arts curriculum. Thirty-three of the individual puzzles also correlate with the areas of mathematics, social studies and science.

In addition to the word search, crossword, and maze puzzles usually found in game books at the elementary level, the activities include proverb puzzles, cryptograms and codes, scrambled words and anagrams, roundabouts, word squares and circles, word ladders, word chains, secret messages, riddles, puns, and a variety of other modes.

For easy use, all of these word puzzles and games are printed in a big 8 1/4" x 11" format that can be photocopied as many times as needed for individual or group use, and organized into the following three sections:

READING & LIBRARY

Section One provides 68 individual reproducibles ranging from "Alphabet Scramble," "Boxed Pairs" and "Silly Paragraph" (Final E), to "Scattergorize," "Shapes and Categories," "Rhyme Time Word Search" and "Proverb Nit-Picking." Also included are 9 stimulating group games, such as "Dictionary Guide Words Race," "What Did I Write?" (with game board and cards), and "Alphabet Game" (with cards).

SPELLING & VOCABULARY

Section Two offers 60 individual puzzle sheets, such as "Dear Tale or Deer Tail?" "Backward and Forward Spelling," "Missing Links: Endings," "Anagram Ladder," and "Word Scramble Secret." In addition, this section features 9 group word games, including "Memory Recall," "Color Beads" (with reproducible game board and cards), and "Spell and Challenge."

LANGUAGE ARTS, MATHEMATICS, SOCIAL STUDIES & SCIENCE

Section Three gives you 41 individual puzzle activities plus 9 more group games with reproducible game components. Here are just a few samples from each content area: "Sentences to Divide and Conquer" (language arts) ... "It All Adds Up" (math) ... "President's Day" (social studies) ... "Punctuation Riddles" (language arts) ... "Do You Know Your Crustaceans?" (science) ... "Spelling with Roman Numerals" (math) ... and "Bugaboo" (science).

Complete answer keys for the individual puzzles are provided at the end, and a special appendix ("Teacher Notes") offers tips on using the games and puzzles with your students and instructions for making and using specific game items such as spinners.

You'll find these Instant Word Games are practical with either a basal or a whole language approach. You can use them to introduce a concept, add to regular lessons, follow-up after teaching or as a reward for early finishers. They will add spice to your classes and give children the stimulating practice they need to develop and maintain skills.

About the Author

Judie L.H. Strouf has taught language arts, reading, English, literature and special education for 27 years in the public schools of Michigan. She also spent a year in England as English Department Head, Chipping Norton Grammar School. Ms. Strouf earned her B.S. from Central Michigan University and her M.A. from Western Michigan University.

THE CENTER FOR APPLIED RESEARCH IN EDUCATION
West Nyack, NY 10994
A Simon & Schuster Company

On the World Wide Web at http://www.phdirect.com

Cover Design by Juan S. DeGuzman

C-635X-2

ISBN 0-87628-635-X

9 780876 286357

90000